F

GEORGE M. HIDY

National Center
for Atmospheric Research

THE WINDS

The Origins and Behavior
of Atmospheric Motion

Published for
The Commission on College Physics

D. VAN NOSTRAND COMPANY, INC.

Princeton, New Jersey

Toronto   *London*   *Melbourne*

Van Nostrand Regional Offices: *New York, Chicago, San Francisco*

D. Van Nostrand Company, Ltd., *London*

D. Van Nostrand Company (Canada), Ltd., *Toronto*

D. Van Nostrand Australia Pty. Ltd., *Melbourne*

PRINTED IN THE UNITED STATES OF AMERICA

Preface

The study of the mechanisms for flow of the earth's fluids forms a significant part of the science called geophysics. With the growing attention to the earth sciences, many students are becoming more interested in the atmosphere and its motion. Because geophysics and its branch, atmospheric dynamics, are increasingly important parts of modern science, students should become better acquainted with the problems and achievements in these fields early in their studies. Unfortunately, the discussion of our planet and the mechanics of its atmosphere is often neglected in elementary texts of physics. As a supplement to these sources, this book has been written to give a brief outline of certain important features of atmospheric motion, and to demonstrate how these features fit into the general framework of classical fluid mechanics. I hope that this book will provide a useful introduction, for students and practicing scientists alike, to some of the basic ideas that are involved in studying the dynamics of the atmosphere.

Sources for the chapters vary from classical work dating back to Greek philosophers to some recent studies by scientists who are presently engaged in atmospheric research. Most of the information in the book comes from published accounts, including books and periodicals in fluid mechanics and meteorology. Because of the introductory nature of this book, I have avoided giving detailed references for much of the background material. It is appropriate, however, to acknowledge four particularly fertile sources of information. Much of the discussion of the principles of fluid mechanics was influenced by Ludwig Prandtl's book, *Essentials of Fluid Dynamics,* and Stanley Corrsin's *Lecture Notes on Introductory Fluid Mechanics.* Applications of the fundamentals to atmospheric motion are discussed comprehensively in R. S. Scorer's book, *Natural Aerodynamics,* and H. R. Byers' text, *General Meteorology.*

The illustrations have been drawn from many sources, and I acknowledge the cooperation of everyone concerned.

The helpful suggestions of many of my colleagues including A. Bainbridge, J. W. Deardorff, W. Fischer, W. Willmarth, and E. J. Plate, are greatly appreciated. I am particularly grateful to the editor of this series for his thoughtful criticisms.

G. M. H.

The photograph on the cover is a picture taken on April 28, 1967 by the ATS-1 synchronous satellite. This spectacular photo shows cloud patterns over the Pacific Ocean, which reveal large vortices in both hemispheres, as well as the intertropical convergence zone near the equator.

Table of Contents

1　*Introduction*

Among the absolutes in man's world are the stars and the weather, and as inescapable as the existence of the weather is the presence of the winds.[1] For the earthbound, there is no deliverance from the winds, whether they be gentle, cooling zephyrs passing over an alpine meadow, or shrieking gales smashing across the North Atlantic.

The ubiquity of winds just constitutes an expression of the restless, quixotic, unceasing motion of the earth's atmosphere. Thus, from the standpoint of physics, the theory of the winds represents nothing more nor less than a problem or a series of problems in fluid dynamics. Such a statement, of course, belies the extraordinarily complicated interplay between the behavior of the air in motion and the many other aspects of atmospheric physics, including the influence of solar radiation and cloud formation.

To understand completely the origin and maintenance of the winds, a vast spectrum of astrophysical and geophysical phenomena must be taken into account. In spite of an infinity of unanswered questions about atmospheric motion, there is still a wealth of information about the earth, its ocean of air, and its distant environment, from which many features of the winds may be explained.

The most important source of information about the winds comes from meteorology,[2] the science of the atmosphere and its

---

[1] Ordinarily in meteorology, the winds refer only to horizontal motion of air. In this book, however, winds will be used to cover both horizontal and vertical flow of air.

[2] An interesting account of the origins of meteorology, and of this science in Elizabethan times, can be found in S. K. Heninger's book, *A Handbook of Renaissance Meteorology* (Duke University Press, Durham, N. C., 1960).

phenomena. In practice, meteorologists are primarily concerned with the weather. The winds are, of course, an integral part of the weather. However, in this book, we shall place emphasis primarily on the dynamics of air motion rather than the various states of hotness, dryness, and storminess of the atmosphere.

CENTURIES OF WIND PHYSICS

Ever since the mythical God of the North winds, *Boreas,* first left his cave home, men have been concerned with atmospheric motion. The beliefs of early men ascribed atmospheric phenomena to divine sources. Primitive weather modification was the realm of the gods or the tribal priests. The weather meddling of the gods is described by Homer about 1000 B.C. In the *Iliad,* for instance, Zeus employed the violence of a thunderstorm to scatter the Greek ships just as Greeks were on the verge of defeating the Trojans. Several examples of God's influence on the weather are found in the Bible. From the *Book of Psalms* (Psalm 107), for example, ". . . they saw the deeds of the Lord, His wondrous works in the deep. For He commanded, and raised the stormy wind, which lifted up the waves of the sea."

The connection between the winds and approaching storms was suspected at the very beginning of man's inquiries about weather. Primitive forecasters developed a variety of gadgets to measure the state of the wind. For example, wind vanes were known to the Chinese and the Egyptians at the dawn of civilization. Furthermore, in Athens, there was a vane located on the famous observatory, the Tower of the Winds, built in the second century, B.C. It is likely that the Greeks used wind vanes at a much earlier date but their origins in this civilization are forever lost in the past.

By the fifth century, B.C., Greek philosophers began to realize that there were natural causes for development of the weather. However, their lack of observational instrumentation and knowledge of fundamental laws of physics caused them to rely only on speculatory explanations of atmospheric phenomena.

One of the first known meteorological theorists was Aristotle. His *Meteorologica,* written about 340 B.C., provided a unified, consistent account of atmospheric processes including the nature of winds, clouds, precipitation, and electrification. Aristotle's earth-centered natural philosophy had a profound effect on meteorology through the sixteenth century. In fact his theories provided the basis for the commonly accepted explanations of atmospheric phenomena of the Renaissance scientists.

Aristotelian theory relied heavily on the interplay and transformations between the four "elements," air, water, fire, and earth. Interestingly enough, these materials compose the heart of modern geophysics. However, along with other of his ancient colleagues, Aristotle failed to master many of the basic principles of physics as we know them today. An inadequate understanding of the complexities of natural phenomena led to inaccurate explanations of all atmospheric processes. For example, Aristotle[3] explains the relation between wind and effects of atmospheric electricity in the following way:

". . . any dry exhalation (wind) that gets trapped when the air is in the process of cooling is forcibly ejected as the clouds condense and it strikes the surrounding clouds, and the noise caused by the impact is in a flame, which some people call Hephaestus' or Hestis' laugh or threat. This noise occurs when the exhalation is hurled bodily against the flame as the logs crack and dry; similarly the windy exhalation in the clouds produces thunder when it strikes a dense cloud formation. . . . As a rule, the ejected wind burns with a fine and gentle fire, and it is then what we call lightning, which occurs when the falling wind appears to us as if it were coloured. Lightning is produced after the impact and so later than thunder, but appears to us to precede it because we see the flash before we hear the noise."

Of course, we believe now that the air motion in a thunderstorm is only indirectly coupled to lightning strokes.

Much of the theoretical meteorologists' efforts in Greece and Rome, and through the sixteenth century were devoted to verification and amplification of Aristotle's ideas. Forecasting was left to the realm of the cults of astrology. However, one notable exception to this rule was the climatological work of the Oxford

[3] Aristotle, *Meteorologica*, trans. by H. D. P. Lee (The Loeb Classical Library, Harvard University Press, Cambridge, Massachusetts, 1952), pp. 225-226.

scholar, William Merle. Merle collected systematically daily weather observations in England from 1337-1344. Although his early efforts were very important, they suffered, of course, from the unavoidable lack of temperature measurements. The thermometer was not to be developed for another 300 years.

A Birth of New Scientific Tools. About 1600, the important basic tools for modern meteorology began to appear. Just after the turn of the seventeenth century, Galileo invented the thermometer. Before another 50 years had passed, his pupil, Evangelista Torricelli, constructed a barometer from a glass tube and a bowl of mercury. At the same time, crude but effective devices for measuring humidity were discovered. During the seventeenth century, philosopher-inventors like Robert Hooke and Christopher Wren in England began to put together packages of instruments for meteorological measurements. One of Hooke's most elaborate devices was a weather clock, an assembly to measure simultaneously time, temperature, pressure, humidity, and rainfall, as well as the magnitude and direction of the wind.

Soon after the invention of the barometer, Renaissance scientists became fascinated to find that changes in barometer readings heralded changes in weather. This feature of the barometric pressure remains a part of modern weather forecasting. However, the early meteorologists, not knowing all of the pressure variations affecting barometer readings, were convinced that this instrument could predict in a foolproof way the type of incoming weather. In fact, Hooke devised a wheel barometer with a pointer and a dial to indicate the rise and fall of mercury. The dial was calibrated to read "change" around 76 cm of mercury, "stormy-rain" at lower pressures, and "fair-dry" at higher pressures. The prognostic attributes have carried over to our present-day household barometers which are labeled in a similar way.

At the same time the quantitative tools for measuring atmospheric motion were being developed, scientists began to keep more extensive records of the winds and the weather. By the end of the seventeenth century, regular local and international records of wind patterns and atmospheric conditions were being kept in regions as far apart as central Europe, England, and even in South Carolina. Information quickly began to disseminate from worker to worker and from country to country, giving atmospheric science the world-wide character that distinguishes it even today.

With the existence of meteorological records, scientists naturally began to try to place an order in the observations. As early as 1625, Francis Bacon tried to trace long-term cycling in comparatively severe seasonal weather. Bacon's efforts signalled the beginnings of many relatively fruitless studies of long-term atmospheric fluctuations. This research is still continuing with no real hope for a definitive end.

Newton's Picture of Dynamics. Paralleling the chain of achievement in experimental sciences, the late seventeenth century produced a hallmark in the development of the theory of classical physics. Influenced by searches of the astronomers Galileo, Brahe, and Kepler for natural laws of the universe, Sir Isaac Newton in 1687 published his monumental *Philosophiae Naturalis Principia Mathematica*. In this widely acclaimed work, Newton reasoned that all bodies, no matter how small or large, responded to specific laws of gravitation and motion.

All of the ideas in the *Principia* are essential features of physics as we know it today. However, two particular principles derived from this work provide the cornerstones of modern meteorology. These are the Law of Conservation of Mass and the Second Law of Motion. The first principle requires that mass can neither be created nor destroyed; it can only be changed from one form into another. The second principle states that a body whose motion is changed by an external force will accelerate in the same direction as the force at a rate proportional to the strength of that force. These two simple statements, in principle, contain the essentials of dynamics of the atmosphere, for they relate mass, force, and changes in velocity to each other.

As significant as it was, Newton's *Principia* did not provide all of the necessary answers. Although the Second Law tells how to equate mass, force and acceleration, it gives few clues about the nature of the forces actually acting on bodies of air. Key principles connecting the properties of air, and connecting energetics to forces remained to be discovered. Although the exact relations between heat and work were not to be found for another 150 years, certain additional information about the nature of gases began to appear at the same time as Newton's work. For example, in 1662 the Irish physicist Robert Boyle found that the volume of a gas is inversely proportional to its pressure if the gas temperature is held constant. A span of nearly a century lapsed before the French physicist Jacques Charles found the companion relation to Boyle's Law. Charles' Law says that the change in the volume of a gas is directly proportional to the change in temperature. With these principles came the notions of the behavior of idealized gases, from which the contraction or expansion of air during cooling or heating could be calculated.

The Laws of Newton, Boyle, and Charles are fundamental principles in physics. The laws of the atmosphere follow from application of these fundamentals. In this sense, atmospheric physics and, of course, all of geophysics and astrophysics are derived sciences. One of the earliest examples of application of the basic principles to the behavior of the winds was attempted by Edmund Halley. Only 24 years after the announcement of Boyle's discovery, Halley, Britain's Astronomer-Royal, published his epochal memoir on the causes of tropical trade winds and monsoons. In this paper, the first meteorological map reporting the prevailing winds in the lower latitudes was discussed. These first-hand observations were combined with theories of atmospheric processes.

To Halley it appeared that the prevailing tropical winds were induced by the action of the sun on air over the equatorial zone. The heated air tended to rise, pulling air inward from the north and south. This concept of motion fits our present theory fairly closely. However, Halley's hypotheses faltered when attempting to explain why the trade winds blew from the northeast in the Northern Hemisphere, and from the southeast in the Southern Hemisphere. He could only explain these observations by suggesting that the tropical winds followed the westward-traveling sun. Some 50 years later George Hadley, a London lawyer, was able to explain the behavior of the tropical belts of winds. Hadley agreed with Halley that solar heating could account for the origins of the trade winds. However, he proposed that the westward flow of air was the result of the west-to-east rotation of the earth. Hadley realized that the earth's surface is moving faster at the equator than it is towards the poles. Therefore, a wind moving towards the equator should lag behind the spinning earth, hitting the equator at a point behind the meridian from which it began. Thus the wind would appear to have a westerly direction from an observer sitting on the earth. Hadley's conclusions are surprisingly close to the current theory, which involves the use of the Coriolis force.

A Tidal Wave of New Ideas in Physics. The works of Halley and Hadley were more or less typical of a new frontier of effort in fundamental and applied science which began to appear in the eighteenth and nineteenth centuries. During this time, important steps were taken beyond the research of Boyle and Charles towards understanding the properties of gases. The English physical chemist, John Dalton, for example, began looking for connections between wind, rain, and the heating of air. He discovered the Law of Partial Pressures in 1790. In this law lies the key to connecting the behavior of a mixture of gases with its individual components. Meteorologists could now calculate the amount of water vapor in air and thus describe mathematically the formation of clouds in the atmosphere.

Along with new knowledge about the behavior of gases, the last piece of the ageless puzzle of the physics of the winds began to be fit into place. Although the connection between heat and motion had long been known, the exact relationships between thermal and kinetic energy were finally formulated by the mid-nineteenth century. About this time, physicists began to realize that the Law of Conservation of Mass might also be true of energy. Perhaps it, too, could neither be created nor consumed, but only could be passed among different forms. The relation between kinetic energy and thermal energy was established in the experiments of the British physicist, James Joule. The most familiar of these experiments is the one in which Joule increased the temperature of a body of water, almost entirely surrounded by insulated walls, by means of a paddle propelled by a falling weight. The result of this experiment was to show an almost exact proportionality between the kinetic energy imparted to the paddle and the rise in water temperature. This result in itself was not too significant. What was important in Joule's work was the fact that the same proportionality was found regardless of the method of transforming energy into the temperature rise in the water. Joule's results then showed that kinetic energy had not been lost from the paddle, but simply transferred into another form, thermal energy.

Soon after Joule had performed his experiments, Joule's principle was put into the form of a law, the First Law of Thermodynamics, or the Law of Conservation of Energy. In effect, this principle gives the relation between heating, the internal energy of a gas, and the work done during its expansion. With this law, the last of the fundamental ideas for understanding the weather and the winds became available.

As rapidly as the new theory of energy was appearing, new knowledge of fluid dynamics was being developed. By the mid-eighteenth century, the Swiss mathematician Leonhard Euler, and the French mathematicians Joseph Lagrange, Pierre Laplace, and Daniel Bernoulli started to examine the consequences of Newton's laws of motion for ideal (frictionless) fluids. The work of Euler was so important that he is considered by many to be the father of hydrodynamics. In the nineteenth century, the analogies between the theory of ideal fluids and field theories of electromagnetism were being developed by the German scientist Hermann von Helmholtz, the Scottish physicist James Maxwell, and the English physicists Lords Rayleigh and Kelvin. During the mid-1800s inconsistencies between the theory for ideal fluids and experimental observations led to new work on the frictional properties of fluids by men such as Sir Osborne Reynolds, C. L. Navier, and G. Stokes.

The rapidly expanding knowledge of the physics of fluids quickly reached the atmospheric scientists. For example, by 1835, Coriolis had layed down the principles of an apparent force related to a rotating framework of reference. But it was the Frenchman, William Ferrell who, in 1856, placed a breath of life in Coriolis' work by explaining Hadley's hypotheses about the earth's rotation and the fields of prevailing winds in the atmosphere.

Meteorological observations continued with increased vigor during the eighteeenth and nineteenth centuries through the extraordinary efforts of amateur and professional scientists. It was soon realized that the understanding of air motion would progress only with exploration of the upper levels of the atmosphere. Hence the eighteenth century sport of ballooning became an important tool to meteorologists. In 1783, the hot air balloon was invented in France by the Montgolfier brothers. Shortly thereafter, Jacques Charles carried a barometer aloft as an altimeter. Only two years later John Jeffries made the first measurements of temperature and barometric pressure up to altitudes of 9000 feet. By the mid-nineteenth century, numerous scientific balloon ascents had been undertaken. Some of the more important ones were made by the British scientist James Glaisher. Between 1862 and 1866, Glaisher made 28 flights. While taking atmospheric measurements in an open gondola at an altitude of 29,000 feet, he nearly was asphyxiated before his half-frozen pilot was able to reach their balloon's release valve.

For the weather at sea, the mariners' log books provided the bulk of systematic information. The weather over continents continued to be recorded by observers located primarily in eastern North America and in western Europe. Watching the weather over land also became a popular pastime of many men, including some famous American statesmen. Benjamin Franklin's contributions to atmospheric electrification are well known, but such political figures as George Washington, Thomas Jefferson, and James Madison also kept weather records. Occasionally, important discoveries were made quite by accident. For instance in 1743, Benjamin Franklin first deduced the prevailing southwest-to-northeast drift of Atlantic coastal storms from information gathered about a storm which obscured his view of an eclipse of the moon. About 80 years later, an inquisitive New England merchant, William Redfield, found that his observations of hurricanes and the information of others concerning these storms fitted a definite pattern. By 1831, Redfield published a historical report advancing the remarkable theory, long since confirmed, that hurricanes have a wind system that spins in a counterclockwise direction with a calm central region, and their winds are extremely intense, even though the movement of the entire storm is quite slow.

Initially, records of weather were only slowly communicated among workers. Therefore their value for practical purposes of weather forecasting was severely limited. With the invention of the telegraph in the 1850s a new potential for weather data networks appeared. The driving force for setting up such a network did not exist until the French and British fleets foundered off Balaklava in a violent storm on November 14, 1854. This disaster could have been averted had news of the impending storm been wired to this Black Sea port. Within months after the Balaklava sinkings, weather networks reporting daily atmospheric conditions were set up in France and in the United States.

The Twentieth Century—New Vistas and a Vast Future. With the rapid expansion of scientific knowledge in the seventeenth to nineteenth centuries, the stage was set for a fantastic new era for progress in the atmospheric sciences during the twentieth century.

The inventions of the radio and other electronic instrumentation have given meteorologists a new array of tools for detailed atmospheric observations. Surface-based stations now report automatically to central locations where incoming atmospheric data are analyzed by high-speed computers and weather maps are produced and sent out two or more times a day. International groups like the World Meteorological Organization have undertaken to organize and establish observational networks on land and at sea all over the globe. The systems of surface stations are being supplemented by routine balloon and aircraft measurements at lower altitudes. The development of high-altitude airplanes, rockets, and artificial satellites has enabled scientists to extend their measurements to the highest levels of the atmosphere.

Along with the fantastic expansion in atmospheric observations during the twentieth century have come substantial developments in the theory of fluid dynamics. New knowledge about fluid flow near boundaries has been found by aerodynamicists such as Ludwig Prandtl in Germany, G. I. Taylor in England, and Theodore Von Karman in the United States.

In our age of specialization, the application of the fundamentals of fluid motion to the atmosphere and to the oceans has given birth to a "new" field of physics, *geophysical fluid mechanics*. Since the turn of the century, scientists too numerous to mention have contributed to our knowledge of this field. It is generally agreed, however, that the efforts of some workers have been especially significant in contributing to the physics of the winds. For example, the nature of systems of planetary winds is better understood as a result of the research of Norway's V. and J. Bjerknes, T. Bergeron, Finland's E. Palmen, and the Swedish-American C. G. Rossby. The behavior of surface layers of the atmosphere is better known from the efforts of such workers as Germany's V. W. Ekman and L. Prandtl, and England's G. I. Taylor and O. G. Sutton.

One of the most important tools to the twentieth century atmospheric physicist has been the high-speed calculating machine. After 1900, workers at the Norwegian Geophysical Institute at Bergen and the British mathematician Lewis Richardson, realized that the complicated mathematics of atmospheric motion and subsequent weather prediction could best be solved by step-by-step numerical calculations. Richardson estimated that, in practice, to compute properly usable results by numerical methods would require a year's work of 64,000 mathematicians calculating 24 hours per day. Shortly after World War II, an electronic contraption for performing such computations was developed. One of the first of these machines was built at Princeton University about 1947 by John Von Neumann. Within the last 15 years, our new technology has allowed the construction of computers which are orders of magnitude larger that Von Neumann's improbable MANIAC. Over the years, scientists have at last developed the techniques that provide firm foundations for numerical analysis of atmospheric motion.

Tracking Down the Mysteries of the Winds. With the basic tools of the trade, we can reasonably expect a future of vast new vistas in the physics of the winds. As we have seen, the building blocks for the theory of atmospheric motion essentially include the thermodynamics of gas mixtures and Newton's laws of mechanics. To make progress in the knowledge of the winds, new observations must be continuously explained by new theoretical ideas. At present, as we shall see later, the average motion of the atmosphere is at least qualitatively understood. The attack of most workers now centers attention on the quixotic daily deviations of the winds from their patterns of average motion. Later we shall discuss a *pot pourri* of possible combinations of air flow which lie within the framework of the mean winds. By way of introduction, however, let us first get a better idea of how the atmosphere keeps itself in a state of agitation.

HOW THE WINDS ARE BORN AND MAINTAINED

The atmosphere can be viewed as a gigantic engine powered by fuel ultimately coming from the sun. The end products of the engine are the winds and the weather. The operation of the engine depends on the feedback of the engine's products and is constrained by the limits of the earth's geometry and the planet's rotation. An important degree of freedom in the power plant is the change in phase of water.

Solar fuel in the form of short waves of radiation impinges continuously on the earth at a rate of $23 \cdot 10^{12}$ horsepower. Over half of the incoming energy is lost by reflection from gas molecules and clouds. Of the remainder, less than 20% is absorbed by the air and the clouds. The radiation that reaches the earth's surface contributes to heating of molecules, which, in turn, reradiate energy at longer infrared wavelengths. The earth radiates energy back to the atmosphere very unevenly. By their very nature, the rivers, oceans, mountains, and deserts cause strong local differences in heat transfer. The uneven distribution of heat causes differences in pressure which in turn induce the machinery of the atmosphere to begin moving. The net effect of the atmospheric motion is ultimately to try to distribute heat uniformly over the world. Basically, warm and cool air mix in all directions in huge masses as warm equatorial air moves towards the poles, and as cold air moves equatorward. This basic circulation creates ultimately the belts of prevailing global winds.

If it were not for clouds and water vapor, the sun's energy would quickly return to space. However, the moisture contained in the air acts as a reflector to infrared radiation and reradiates considerable energy back to the earth. This game of trapping longer waves of energy, but letting shorter wavelength radiation pass, is called the "greenhouse effect" in analogy to the similar function of the glass roof of a greenhouse.

One might say that the winds originate near the earth's equator. The tropics receive much more solar energy per unit area of surface than the polar regions. Hence, the tropical regions serve as a boiler room for the atmospheric engine where the fuel is added to keep the air's machinery going. Much of the input energy is eventually returned to space in the polar regions where heat radiates away from the earth faster than it is received by the sun.

Intervening between the input of fuel and the conversion of a tiny fraction of its energy to the winds are an infinity of transportations and transformations. The atmospheric engine is exceedingly inefficient. Only 1 or 2% of the inflow of thermal energy sustains air motion. The rest is returned to space.

Water in the air not only reflects infrared radiation back to the earth, but also it stores energy. Water vapor riding on the winds provides an extremely important vehicle for transporting heat. As solar radiation hits the oceans, water is warmed below, and at the surface. Millions of tons of water from the ocean's surface enter the atmosphere as vapor as a result of evaporation. The latent heat contained in water vapor is transferred to the atmosphere when air cools to the point where the vapor can condense to form clouds. Huge quantities of energy are put into the atmosphere this way. In fact about 80% of the fuel to drive the atmosphere is initially latent in water vapor. Because 75% of the earth is covered by water, the importance of the oceans to meteorology becomes quite clear. Since most of the equatorial regions are covered by water, a large part of the latent heat is delivered to the atmosphere in these zones. Scientists even have used the analogy of a fuel pump for describing the role in atmospheric circulation of the huge rows of towering cumulus clouds observed over the tropical oceans.

Giant Patterns of Convective Circulation. The work of the atmospheric engine goes towards pushing thermal energy from the source regions in the tropics to the sink zones at the poles. This exchange is largely carried out by the air motion itself—called *convection.* One can imagine for simplicity that the air flow is analogous to the circulation caused by a hot stove in a closed room. The warmer moisture-laden equatorial air rises from the tropical stove towards the ceiling, while cooler air flows in from the northern and southern edges of the room. As the warm air travels poleward or "wallward" along the ceiling, it cools and sinks towards the floor, completing the circulation. The added effect of the earth's rotation tends to skew the pattern of mean motion away from the north-south flow, towards the eastward and westward directions.

Although the convective circulation pattern is simple in principle, it is complicated by the influences of feedback from already existing winds and from the landscape. For example, mountain ranges can overturn the atmosphere and cause less dense air to flow under more dense air. The pressure of the air does not decrease smoothly from the equator to the poles, but in reality it varies strongly as a result of contrasts in topography. Random fluctuations in temperature and pressure cause the infinite variety of departures from the mean flow in the form of currents, whirlpools and eruptions. The transient criss-cross of air flow over the globe represents a set of fluctuating motions superimposed upon the mean thermal circulation. These fluctuations constitute the highly variable, unreliable patterns of daily winds that are so important to human life and are so difficult to place on a scientific basis.

SOME CHARACTERISTIC FEATURES
OF ATMOSPHERIC MOTION

Despite the outwardly dissimilar behavior of atmospheric motion, there are certain phenomenological features which serve as common denominators for the physics of the winds. These are: (a) extremes in scale or size factors, (b) layering of the air, (c) effects of the earth's spin, (d) lumpiness and streakiness, and (e) eddying. We shall see later that these characteristics will arise time after time in describing the nature of the winds. Therefore, let us briefly outline their meaning and implications.

Size or Scaling Factors. What is meant by the scale of fluid motion? Scale generally refers to the dimensions of a system. One logical dimension, of course, consists of length. Normally the basic mechanical and thermodynamic dimensions of length [L], mass [M], time [T], and temperature [θ] provide the framework for scaling fluid flow. When a current is scaled it is sized relative to other parts of the fluid motion. Sizing can then be referred to the basic dimensions or to dimensions such as velocity $[LT^{-1}]$ or energy $[ML^2T^{-2}]$ which can be derived from the basic dimensions. As an example, we can distinguish a hurricane from a tornado by scale factors alone. The length scale for the hurricane vortex is hundreds of kilometers while the characteristic length of a tornado is about one kilometer. On the other hand the maximum tangential speed of winds in the hurricane is about 40 meters per second (m sec^{-1}) while the tornado vortex may attain air velocities of 100 m sec^{-1}.

All systems of fluid flow have certain scale factors. The feature that distinguishes atmospheric motion from other kinds of fluid flow is its extremely wide range of interacting scales. In geophysical problems for instance, the length scale of motion varies from tenths of millimeters to thousands of kilometers, while the time scale varies between microseconds and years. These ranges are very large compared with the ranges of lengths and times which workers ordinarily encounter in engineering problems or in the laboratory.

Because of the complexities in the behavior of winds, dynamicists have attempted to analyze air motion by breaking the net phenomenon into pieces of limited size. Unfortunately the coupling of motions on many different scales causes the total motion to react in a spectacularly different way from the expectations of the sum of its pieces. In spite of this difficulty, the simplification of isolating one scale of motion from another has been invaluable to the study of the dynamics of particularly striking examples of air motion such as the jet stream or a tornado vortex.

Layering or Stratification. When layers of fluids of different density exist in a gravitational field, the fluids tend to adjust themselves in such a way that they will ultimately come to equilibrium. Under the influence of gravity only, motion will tend to stop after the heavy fluid sinks to the bottom of the container, or after the layers become mixed to form a fluid of uniform density. Convection in the atmosphere is associated with this tendency towards an equilibrium condition. The potential energy of a mass of heavy fluid lying on top of light fluid is a key factor in the chains of energy transformation in the atmosphere. The structure of the air density at any particular location is closely tied to the intensity of vertical and horizontal flow. Sharp contrasts in air density are often observed in nearly all scales of atmospheric motion.

The Earth's Spin. In discussing the chain of reasoning leading to the present picture of wind fields, we observed that the earth's rotation plays a major role in the planetary scale motion. The tendency for meridional circulation to swing towards an east-west direction is tied with the effect of the spinning earth on which we exist. The reason for this behavior is associated with our frame of reference. If an observer watches the motion of the air from the earth, he must take into account the fact that both he and the atmosphere rotate with respect to the stars. That is, the observer's natural system of coordinates on the earth is moving with respect to a system "fixed" on the position of the stars. The effect of the moving coordinates is to add an apparent force, the *Coriolis force,* to the action of forces acting on a body of air. The balances of the Coriolis force, friction, pressure differences, and gravity determine the magnitude and velocity of the winds.

Lumpiness and Streakiness. The lumpy and streaky nature of atmospheric motion can easily be seen in the ever-present clouds passing overhead. The tendency for strong vertical motion to develop into cells surrounded by relatively still air can easily be observed in the formation and growth of cumulus clouds [e.g., Plate I(A)]. Bumps associated with non-uniformities in vertical air motion can even be seen from an airplane flying over layers of clouds [Plate I(B)].

The tendency to form strong currents of air in quiescent fluid is not limited to vertical motion. The jet stream blowing at altitudes of 10 kilometers (km) in the mid-latitudes is a familiar feature of the television weatherman's discourse. Streaks of high cirrus clouds as shown in Plate III often give away the position of strong horizontal currents. Streakiness can even be combined with lumpiness. Often lines or streets of tiny cumulus billows are observed over the tropical oceans as indicated in Plate II(A).

The lumpy, streaky nature of the atmosphere is comparatively poorly understood at present. The presence of these familiar inhomogeneities makes the task of putting the puzzle of the winds together very difficult.

Eddying. Associated with the lumpiness and streakiness of the atmosphere are the wide variety of eddies or whirls ranging in scale from the spectacular to the plebeian. Perhaps the most well known examples of spinning motion are the tornadoes and hurricanes. Once again, the clouds provide a picture of the whereabouts of these severe storms as shown in Plates V and VI. Eddying motion is also a common feature of the tiny scale air motion as traced by smoke from a cigarette [Plate VII(A)] or the plume of a smoke stake [Plate VII(B)].

Much of the lumpiness in air is associated with *turbulence.* This kind of flow is marked by the irregularity and the transiency of its rotational motion and its consequent power of dispersing material carried by the air. The curling motion in the rising cigarette plume [Plate VII(A)] becomes irregular, signaling the onset of turbulent motion. Simultaneously, the smoke particles are dispersed rapidly into the surrounding air.

We often experience turbulent air motion outdoors on a windy day. The gusts or bursts of the wind that we feel are part of the large turbulent eddies which sweep past us. The beautiful undulations of fields of grain under conditions of apparently steady wind are also associated with the rolling turbulent eddies as they follow the mean wind over the ground.

With the groundwork completed, the stage is now set for the parade of characters who play the various roles in the story of the physics of atmospheric motion. Because the study of the winds still remains basically an observational science, we shall begin by looking at the techniques for measuring air motion in more detail. After discussing the mean vertical structure of the atmosphere and the nature of the forces acting on bodies of air, we shall return to the picture of average horizontal distribution of winds. At last, we shall take up a few examples of the more interesting fluctuations in the average air flow. By traveling down the ladder of scales of motion, it will be possible to get a brief glimpse of the winds from the giant planetary undulations to the tiny will-o'-the-wisp eddies of turbulence.

Although we shall mention briefly one or two observational aspects of the upper atmosphere in the next two chapters, we will be concerned in this book primarily with air flow below about 10 km altitude.

2 *Observing the Atmosphere in Motion*

As primitive man began to look upwards through the atmosphere, he must have recognized very quickly that the winds were connected in some way to changing weather. From this elemental idea came the will to find or to construct useful indicators for wind direction and speed.

DEVICES FOR WIND MEASUREMENT

Natural Indicators. In the absence of meteorological instruments, the ancient philosophers could always fall back upon the innumerable natural wind indicators which surrounded them. For instance, the trees and other vegetation offer an observer information about the direction of both the prevailing and instantaneous air motion. Travelers along the California sea coast, or anyone who has walked along high ridges of the Rocky Mountains can see clearly the direction of the prevailing westerly winds marked indelibly on the trees bent towards the east with branchless sides turned west. The instantaneous motion of gusts produce, for example, beautiful wavy undulations on a sea of wheat or grass on the plains. Of course, an ingenious fellow could even estimate the relative magnitude of the air flow by watching the degree of bending a sapling or a blade of grass takes on as it yields to the wind.

Another natural signal for the velocity and direction of winds has been known to the mariners for years. The height of waves at sea and the direction of their propagation are directly connected with atmospheric motion. At first, one would guess that waves always are pushed forward with their crests perpendicular to the wind direction. In fact, waves can propagate on water in any direction to the mean wind. What a surprise this observation must have been to the perceptive seafarer. Fortunately, small ocean waves tend to grow fastest in a direction nearly perpendicular to the wind so that the use of waves as an indicator for air flow is often still reasonably good.

Perhaps one of the more spectacular indicators of the enormous kaleidoscope of atmospheric motion lies in the telltale pictures portrayed by the clouds. The writings of Aristotle certainly indicate that the connection between the winds and cloud patterns was at least recognized by the early naturalists by their observations.

They realized how the violent, boiling air motion in thunderstorms was pictured by the beautiful puffy turrets of a cumulonimbus cloud [Plate I(A)]. Imagine what their delight might have been, however, had they been able to uncover the relation, for example, between the giant lee waves and lenticular clouds seen behind mountains (Plate IV), or the high cirrus clouds shown in Plate III which betray the presence of the extraordinarily powerful currents of the upper atmosphere.

Although the natural indicators for wind have been important in qualitatively understanding how air motion behaves, it always is necessary to carry an observational program farther towards quantitative results by making use of well-designed measuring devices. Perhaps the most portable and accessible instrument for wind direction is the wet finger. A moistened finger is cooled most rapidly by evaporation on the side facing the wind. The wind vane, the flag, and the pioneer airman's wind sock also provide simple and useful indicators. However, man's abilities of inventiveness have supplied us with an incredible variety of much more sophisticated contrivances for wind measurement through the centuries. These developments, of course, depended to a large extent on a continuing better understanding of the properties of air and the forces which act upon this gas.

Measurement of Air Properties. As masses of cool or warm air move over a station on the earth's surface, instruments which record air properties such as pressure, temperature, and humidity will change their readings. Similarly, such instruments located at different places will record different values for such properties depending on local atmospheric conditions. These variations in time and in space reflect the character of the weather over a geographical region, and, as we shall see later, can be connected to atmospheric motion. With sufficient data for temperature, humidity, and pressure changes from meteorological stations, it is possible to construct empirical relations between atmospheric properties and the winds and weather. This technique is precisely how the germ of meteorological science developed centuries ago, and it largely provides the cornerstones for some of the methods of weather forecasting used today.

In making measurements of atmospheric properties, attention still is centered on the pressure of the atmosphere. One of the most common devices for gauging pressure is the mercury barometer. This instrument consists simply of a tube, closed at one end, which is first filled completely with mercury. The tube is up-ended to a vertical position in a pool of mercury. The column of mercury will then drop, leaving a vacuum at the top of the tube. The product of the height of the column, the density of mercury, and the gravitational constant will equal the force per unit surface area, or the pressure exerted on the earth's surface by the atmosphere. At sea level, the height of mercury would be approximately 76.0 cm. The density of mercury is 13.6 gm cm^{-3} at 0°C, hence the pressure p of the atmosphere at sea level, 0°C, is approximately

$$p = 76.0 \text{ cm} \cdot 13.6 \text{ gm cm}^{-3} \cdot 980 \text{ cm sec}^{-2} = 1.01 \cdot 10^6 \text{ dyne cm}^{-2}.$$

This value of pressure is equivalent to *one atmosphere.* In geophysics the unit *bar,* which is equal to 76 cm Hg, may be used. Meteorologists often refer to pressure in *millibars,* or 0.001 bar.

Several other devices are frequently used to measure atmospheric pressure. Two favorites are the *aneroid barometer,* and the pressure transducer. The aneroid instrument is just an evacuated cylindrical metal box, whose top becomes slightly deformed with changes in atmospheric pressure. A mechanism is attached to the top that converts the deformation into deflections of a pointer, which may be designed to read on a calibrated scale. The *pressure transducer* consists of an electro-mechanical device through which the pressure signal is converted to an electrical signal. In most pressure transducers, the action of pressure causes a displacement in a spring. This displacement causes a change in an electrical property such as the resistance of a potentiometer, the capacitance between two plates, the inductance of a wire coil, or the piezoelectric property of a crystal.

Devices for measuring the temperature of air are equally as numerous and varied as barometric instruments. Some sensors that are commonly used include (a) the old-fashioned *liquid-in-glass thermometer*, (b) the *resistance thermometer* and the *thermistor*, which utilize the effect of small changes with temperature in the electrical resistance of materials and, (c) *thermocouples*, which employ the well-known thermoelectric effect.

Measurement of moisture in air also can be done in numerous ways. One of the simplest humidity instruments is the *wet bulb thermometer*. This device utilizes the "wet finger" principle; i.e., the cooling or temperature reduction that one experiences on the extended wet finger can be related to the moisture content in the air moving past the finger. Comparison between the difference in temperature measured by a dry thermometer and one whose bulb is wrapped with wet string or cloth can be related to moisture content using well-established tables or calibration curves.[1]

Other hygrometric devices that are often found in meteorological stations include units which adsorb water vapor in definite amounts. Such sensors include animal hair, and thin films of materials like lithium chloride or aluminum oxide. Water vapor content can also be measured spectroscopically by examining the absorption of radiation by water in a gas in the far-infrared region corresponding to electromagnetic wavelengths of ~ 1.37 microns. Hygrometers even have been designed which can use measures of very small changes with moisture content in the refractive index of air.

[1] See, for example, *Handbook of Chemistry and Physics,* C. D. Hodgman, Ed. (Chemical Rubber Publ. Co., Cleveland, Ohio, 1965).

Anemometry. Although it is possible to infer the speed and (sometimes) the direction of winds from changes in atmospheric properties, it is often desirable to obtain more direct measures of atmospheric motion. The measurement of air flow is called *anemometry*. There are essentially five different kinds of instruments which are used to measure the winds. These are: (a) the cup anemometer, (b) the thrust anemometer, (c) the pitot tube, (d) the hot wire anemometer, and (e) the sonic anemometer. The first three rely on the action of the force exerted by the wind on a body. However, the last two work on quite different principles.

A typical *cup anemometer* is sketched in Fig. 2-1. This instru-

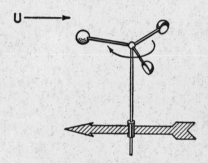

FIG. 2-1   A cup anemometer.

ment can often be seen around airports, especially small ones. It resembles a child's windmill toy, and in fact works just like the toy. As the wind blows, it pushes on the cups and imparts a spin to the star-shaped support for the cups. The rotational speed of the support can be calibrated to read wind speed. Since the cup anemometer is not directionally sensitive, this device is usually combined with a vane so that both velocity and direction of the wind can be measured.

The *thrust anemometer* simply consists of a sphere suspended on a thin shaft, as shown in Fig. 2-2. As the wind blows harder and harder, the drag force on the sphere will increase, and the sphere will be deflected horizontally more and more. The deflection of the sphere is transmitted through the support shaft to a mechanism which records the deflection. The movement of the

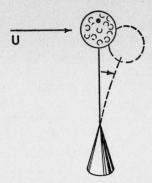

FIG. 2-2   Thrust anemometer.

sphere can be calibrated against a standard device to give values
of wind speed. Sophisticated sensing of the sphere support in different directions also can provide an indication of wind direction.

The *pitot tube* has been used for many years to measure the
speed of aircraft relative to the surrounding air. It is equally useful for measuring wind speed on the ground. The pitot tube is
really two tubes, one inside the other, as shown in Fig. 2-3. The

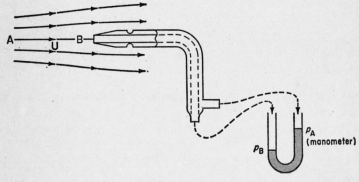

Fig. 2-3   Pitot tube.

outside tube has tiny holes drilled in it, aligned in a direction perpendicular to the air flow. The inner tube is open to the wind
in front. The inner and outer tubes are connected to a manometer, which measures differences in pressure. The inner tube fac-

ing the air flow feels the effect of a greater pressure than the outer tube. The pressure difference between the two tubes is shown on the manometer, and is dependent on the air velocity. This effect can be observed easily with a simple experiment. Open your hand, place it palm up several centimeters from your mouth, and blow on your hand. You can feel the wind strongly on the palm of your hand, but not on the edges of your fingers, which are faced perpendicular to the air flow. This difference is exactly what the pitot tube measures. Later in Chapter 4, we shall discuss Bernoulli's theory, and we shall see how this relation predicts the behavior of the pitot tube.

In contrast to devices for measuring the action of the wind force, the *hot-wire anemometer* relies on a principle analogous to the "wet finger" technique. Instead of indicating a temperature difference between flowing air and a wet surface resulting from evaporation, this device indicates only the rate of transfer of heat from a hot wire to a flowing stream. When a very thin heated wire is placed in flowing air, heat is transported to the gas at a speed which depends on the local air motion. Although this remarkable sensor is quite simple in principle, its use in practice is rather complicated. In spite of its complex nature, this anemometer is an extremely useful tool to the aerodynamicist because of its potential sensitivity to wind direction and its fast response to small changes in air motion.

The last kind of anemometer, the *sonic anemometer,* has begun to be developed just recently. This unique instrument measures the very small changes in relative speed of propagation of acoustic waves with small variations in air flow. Typically, a tiny sound-wave generator (T) and a receiver (R) are placed on arms about 1 meter apart as shown in Fig. 2-4. Variations in the component of air motion parallel to the path of the acoustic waves cause differences in the propagation of the signal transmitted to the receiver. These differences are reflected in a change in phase of the waves traveling between (T) and (R). The sonic anemometer potentially has considerable value for measuring small transverse components (V) of an air flow where main stream is directed across the path of the acoustic waves (U). Because the sonic anemometer is still being developed, it remains primarily a research tool at present.

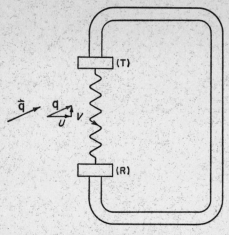

FIG. 2-4   Sonic anemometer.

Radar Observations. Atmospheric motion may also be observed by indirect sensors. It is possible to link, for example, the reflection and scattering of beams of electromagnetic waves to air flow. The use of radar provides an interesting illustration of this technique.

After World War II, meteorologists began to experiment with the use of radar for atmospheric observations. Radar denotes the art of detecting by means of echoes of radio waves the presence of objects, determining their direction and range, recognizing their character, and applying the acquired data. For the meteorologist, this implies that the "object" is anything in the atmosphere or its boundaries that returns to a receiver a detectable signal of electromagnetic energy. This can include consideration of reflection from the earth's surface, cloud particles, atmospheric dust, and zones of large differences in refractive index of air. Radar has provided useful information about the development of clouds, and thunderstorm systems as well as larger scale atmospheric disturbances. A typical example of a radar picture of a large storm is shown in Plate V(B). This is a photograph of a radar trace of a spinning wind pattern of Hurricane "Betsy." The receiver is picking up back-scattered radiation from the clouds associated with the storm. It is interesting to see how this picture resembles the vortex pattern of clouds in Hurricane Betsy as photographed by Tiros VIII satellite [Plate V(C)].

Wind patterns also can be studied directly using radar. For example, the motion of small strips of aluminum foil, called *chaff*, dropped from a plane, can be traced for considerable distance in the atmosphere. The reflection of signals by the moving chaff is observed easily on a radar receiver.

GEOGRAPHIC OBSERVATIONS OF AIR FLOW

Ground Stations. Once the tools for measuring atmospheric properties are available, the observing stations must be set up to gather data for study. Traditionally, the observer of the atmosphere has been confined to the earth's surface. However, in recent years there has been an ever-increasing desire to reach higher and higher into the atmosphere using different kinds of support vehicles. Nevertheless, even today the surface-based observing station still provides the backbone of the vast worldwide network for observing atmospheric motion.

On land, typical modern surface stations would include instruments for recording barometric pressure, air temperature, and humidity, as well as wind speed and direction. Many of these stations may be operated automatically without an observer present. In the Northern Hemisphere, particularly in the United States and in Europe, information from land-based stations of this type are scattered on a large network of about 1000 km spacing, called *synoptic scale;* a few regions have stations more closely spaced. Continuous data for changes in the atmosphere are funneled to central offices of various weather agencies such as the U.S. Weather Bureau. The data are processed rapidly in these centers by high-speed computers, and the results in the form of weather maps are transmitted to local weather forecasters. Unfortunately, the observing stations in the Southern Hemisphere are much more widely scattered, and consequently less is known about the behavior of the atmosphere in these regions.

Since water makes up a major portion of the earth's surface, it is essential to obtain as much information as possible about atmospheric motion over the vast reaches of the oceans. Observations are much more difficult to obtain on the oceans. There are some weather ships maintained by various governments, and a few fixed buoys which automatically record and transmit weather data. However, many of the observations come from non-scientific ships traveling regularly between landfalls. Without trained observers, the crews of these "ships of opportunity" provide weather information of widely varying quality. Hence, receiving agencies like the Weather Bureau have had to devise elaborate statistical schemes for deducing reasonably reliable average changes in the atmosphere over the oceans.[2]

Since ships travel along relatively well established routes, there remain substantial regions of the ocean basins, especially in the Southern Hemisphere and in the Arctic regions, where virtually no systematic weather data are available. To remedy the problem of filling gaps in land- and sea-based data, international cooperative organizations for obtaining and exchanging information such as the World Meteorological Organization (WMO) have been established. Furthermore, cooperative scientific expeditions have been organized in connection with the International Geophysical Year (IGY) programs in 1957-1958, and the 1962-1964 Indian Ocean Expedition, originating in 1959 with the Scientific Committee on Oceanic Research (SCOR).

Airborne Measurements. The development of ballooning, and the invention of airplanes and rockets have enabled men to explore the upper atmosphere to seek better first hand information about atmospheric motion.

Balloons provide an ideal vehicle for studying the winds because they are cheap, relatively easy to track, and tend to be carried along by the air motion during ascent. Wind drift with altitude can be traced visually with a small balloon carrying no instruments (pilot balloons). Changes in azimuth and altitude angles of the little balloon as read with a theodolite (similar to a surveyor's transit) are used to infer the wind patterns at upper

[2] In the folklore evolving from stories of the methods of tracking storms over the oceans, the custom of naming tropical cyclones for girls seems to have originated during World War II. This suggestion evidently stems from the whimsical activities of a junior meteorologist of the U.S. Weather Bureau in George Stewart's novel *Storm.*

levels. Pilot balloon soundings have become routine measurements for many surface stations.

Packages of meteorological instruments can be carried aloft by tethered balloons, kites, or a combination of these two. Information about atmospheric properties and wind speed can then be returned to the ground observer for recording.

In the 1930s inexpensive instrument packages for measuring pressure, temperature, and humidity began to be launched by free balloon. This instrumentation includes a small battery-powered radio so that data can be continuously transmitted to a ground station. These balloon systems, called *radio sondes,* have been employed extensively in recent years for upper air soundings. Radio sonde results have also been improved by adding a radio direction finder to the receiving station. Using this equipment, the sonde's motion with the wind can be tracked in a manner similar to the pilot balloon.

Since the early pioneering days of James Glaisher, large balloons have been used to carry scientists higher and higher into the atmosphere. The present record of 31 km for manned ascents was made by D. G. Simons in a $8.5 \cdot 10^7$ liter balloon launched from Cosby, Minnesota in 1957. An unmanned balloon of the same volume capacity also has carried instruments to an altitude of about 33 km over a period of about 33.5 hours. As a result of these kinds of high-altitude ascents, meteorologists began to learn for the first time of extraordinary 150 mph winds blowing in the regions of 30 km altitude.

Ballooning continues to intrigue scientists with its possibilities for studying the upper-level winds. The demonstration that the Japanese during World War II could deliver incendiary weapons by balloons traveling half way around the world from the Western Pacific to the west coast of the United States has just begun to be exploited by meteorologists. Special balloon packages carrying instruments and powerful radio transmitters have been designed to ascend and remain at a constant altitude. These vehicles are reasonably stable at altitude and can ride the winds for great distances. By tracking them through many radio stations while they travel around the earth, they can provide exceedingly valuable information of the wind and temperature fields. Until recently, these balloon systems have required large volume capacity and have carried rather expensive equipment. However, a new inexpensive balloon instrument package developed by V. Lally and his colleagues at the National Center for Atmospheric Research may make constant-level ballooning nearly as routine as the little pilot balloon.

Aircraft have been applied extensively since World War I as platforms for carrying meteorological instruments. By virtue of its size and propulsive power, the airplane can carry aloft much more elaborate and sophisticated equipment, including radar, than can balloons or kites. However, airplanes are considerably more expensive to maintain and fly than most balloon systems, so careful planning must go into scientific ventures using planes.

Airplanes have allowed meteorologists to explore the atmosphere over relatively short periods from altitudes of a few meters to over 35 km. Large quantities of fundamental knowledge about the properties of the atmosphere and the patterns of winds have been obtained by research flights. One of the better known examples of these studies is the program of the U. S. military air arms and the Weather Bureau's National Hurricane Center in Florida. The spectacular pictures obtained by pilots flying near and through hurricanes are familiar to all of us. A good example is the photo in Plate V(A) of the eye of Hurricane Betsy, taken from a U. S. Air Force aircraft.

By accident, observations also have provided many new facts about high-altitude winds. A well-known illustration is the discovery of the strong westerly currents of the jet stream located in the mid-latitudes at altitudes above 5 km. These systems of high winds were found as bomber pilots began to fly at higher altitudes during World War II.

Rocket and Satellite Meteorology. An upper limit in height of about 35 km clearly developed in man's exploration of the atmosphere by balloon, or by conventional aircraft. To reach beyond this limit, scientists have begun to utilize rockets and artificial satellites. Before World War II, the employment of these vehicles lay largely in the imaginative realm of Buck Rogers, and in other science fiction. However, we are actually seeing today the reality of the rocket exploration of the very limits of the earth's atmosphere as well as the study of the environment of other planets.

Beginning about 1945, U. S. scientists started to use V-2, Aerobee, and Viking rockets to probe the atmosphere above 100 km. About the same time, similar soundings were being undertaken in the Soviet Union. Later, during the IGY, meteorological rocket research became truly international with advent of Canadian, British, Australian, French, and Japanese programs. During the IGY, and subsequently, more extensive rocket observations have been made, particularly with small rockets rising to altitudes below 100 km.

By 1959, the U. S. Meteorological Rocket Network had been established, in which four stations fired small rockets into the atmosphere on a regular synoptic basis. Since 1959 four other stations have been added, and regular probes are continuing to be made to altitudes of about 60 km. Through the international cooperation of organizations like WMO, the Committee on Space Research (COSPAR), and the International Union of Geodesy and Geophysics (IUGG), the embryo of a world-wide rocket-sounding network now is beginning to appear.

Rocket instrumentation basically follows the traditional approaches. Observations have been obtained by (a) direct measurement by instruments on the vehicle, and subsequent transmission to the ground, (b) direct measurement from instruments separated from the rocket and return to the ground by parachute, (c) ejection of a tracer such as chaff or sodium vapor which can be observed visually, by radar, or other ground-based instruments, and (d) sending an impulse, such as a grenade blast, from the vehicle to the ground, and observing the characteristics of the impulse's propagation through successive layers of the atmosphere.

Although the rocket soundings have not been too numerous, they have given us some brilliant, but all too brief glimpses of the incredible variety of conditions in the very high atmosphere. As a beginning of this new era in meteorology, however, rockets already have enabled scientists to construct weather charts over the North American continent at the 45 and 60 km levels. There is now definite evidence from rocket data that remarkable changes can occur high in the atmosphere, and can be transmitted downward to involve the lower atmosphere. Last but not least, the rocket results have indicated that a strange region exists at 105 km where there is a sudden transitional layer between restless turbulent agitation and processes of molecular diffusion. In this same region, scientists have found that there are exceedingly strong differences in wind speed with altitude. For example, changes of over 100 m sec^{-1} seem to occur over height intervals less than 5 km.

Rockets have also been utilized to launch the now famous meteorological satellites, such as the TIROS and the NIMBUS series. The door to applications of satellites for study of the atmosphere is just opening. However, the potential for these devices has been displayed very well in the beautiful mosaic pictures of world cloud cover, and in the interesting measurements obtained on solar-earth radiation. Good examples of satellite photography are shown in Plates II(B) and V(C).

The door to the upper atmosphere has been opened by new technological devices. But the continued utilization and thorough study of the mountain of new observations and data must proceed before a complete understanding of the atmosphere will become available.

Having outlined some of the tools of the observational trade of wind study, let us next take up some of the important theoretical ideas to establish the remainder of the foundation for discussing the great variety of wind patterns observed in the earth's lower atmosphere.

3 *The Atmosphere at Rest*

Although we are most aware of the vigorous movements of the atmosphere that carry masses of air from one spot on the earth's surface to another, the atmosphere as a whole has to remain nearly in a state of equilibrium. If it did not, the atmosphere might spin away into space, or collapse into a thin layer of fluid pressed close to the planet. In the simplest approximation, a column of air over a reasonably small region of the earth's surface can be considered a fluid at rest. Hence we can examine the structure of such a column, in terms of the variation of pressure or density with height for example, by using the principles of thermodynamics and hydrostatics. To some extent, even the local vertical movement of the atmosphere sometimes can be treated in terms of small disturbances from static equilibrium.

PROPERTIES OF GASES AT EQUILIBRIUM

Thermodynamics tells us that the properties of a gas such as temperature, density, and pressure are related to each other through an equation of state. Near the earth's surface, there are no extremes in atmospheric pressure and temperature. Therefore the Laws of Boyle and Charles, and hence the equation of state for ideal gases, are applicable. The composition of the atmosphere varies from place to place with respect to trace components including water vapor, carbon dioxide, helium, and argon. However, these gases generally make up less than 4% of the total gas in air and their local variations result in only very small changes

33

in the density of the air. Therefore, as a first approximation the atmosphere is considered a "pure," ideal gas whose equation of state is:

$$\frac{p}{\rho} = \frac{R}{M} T, \tag{3.1}$$

where p is pressure, having dimensions $[ML^{-1}T^{-2}]$, ρ denotes the mass density, with dimensions $[ML^{-3}]$, T is the absolute temperature ($^\circ$ Kelvin), M represents the average molecular weight of air, and R is 8.314 (newton meter) (kg mole)$^{-1}$ ($^\circ$K)$^{-1}$. The addition of moisture in air can be accounted for by adjustment of M. Meteorologists often use another constant R' defined as

$$R' \equiv R/M.$$

For dry air at sea level, $M = 28.97$ gm(g-mole)$^{-1}$, and R' becomes $2.867 \cdot 10^2$ (m)^2(sec)$^{-2}$($^\circ$K)$^{-1}$.

Gravity and Pressure. Gravity acts on the mass of the atmosphere in such a way that the closer the air is to the earth the more compressed it becomes. That is, there are fewer molecules of gas in each unit volume of air the higher the altitude above the earth's surface. The density of air continually decreases with altitude as indicated by the dashed line in Fig. 3-1. Above 20 km, the air becomes very "thin," and there is little oxygen left to sustain life. At 90 km, the density[1] is only $4 \cdot 10^{-9}$ gm/cm^3 as compared to $1.3 \cdot 10^{-3}$ gm/cm^3 at sea level.

If we disregard any changes horizontally in pressure, we can write the relation between air pressure and gravity from a knowledge of statics. In fluids at rest, we know that the change in pressure over an increment of height is equal to the product of the density times the gravitational acceleration g. If the height z is measured upward as positive, g is negative, then

$$\frac{dp}{dz} = -\rho g. \tag{3.2}$$

This relation is, of course, the old familiar hydrostatic equation. It provides the essential information for calculating the vertical distribution of atmospheric pressure at equilibrium.

[1] Above 90 km altitude, the average molecular weight of air begins to decrease. This arises chiefly because oxygen is dissociated into atomic species (O) by ultraviolet radiation.

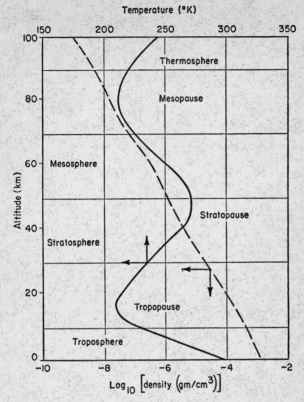

FIG. 3-1 Average vertical distributions of temperature and density in the earth's atmosphere based on data from "The Rocket Panel" (The Upper Atmosphere Rocket Research Panel), Phys. Rev. 88, 1027-1032 (1952).

The pressure of the gas is related to its density and temperature through the equation of state. Hence to obtain the vertical profile of pressure, the density in the hydrostatic relation is replaced by the ratio $p/R'T$. Provided that the gravitational acceleration is assumed a constant, Eq. (3.2) in integrated form becomes the *barometric equation*:

$$z - z_0 = R'/g \int_{p_0}^{p} T d \ln p. \qquad (3.3)$$

The reference height z_0 and the pressure p_0 are ordinarily taken at the earth's surface. To complete the relation for pressure in the atmosphere, the vertical temperature distribution must be known.

Mean Vertical Distributions of Temperature and Pressure. The average variation in temperature of air has been measured directly by balloon ascents up to about 35 km altitude. Above this point, the temperature is deduced from measurements of pressure and density. The present picture of the vertical distribution of temperature up to 100 km altitude in the mid-latitudes is shown by the solid line in Fig. 3-1. This curve will differ somewhat for the polar and equatorial regions. However, the kinks associated with different characteristic layers will tend to remain even though they may be more poorly defined at some times than at others. The lower atmosphere, called the *troposphere,* is characterized by a zone of temperature decrease with altitude. The rate of change in temperature with height is referred to as the *lapse rate.* Above the top of the troposphere, an isothermal region in the lower stratosphere is observed. The beginning of this zone is known as the *tropopause.* High in the stratosphere, the temperature begins to rise to another zone of constant temperature at the *stratopause.* Above the stratopause, in the *mesosphere,* there is a decrease in temperature again up to about 80 km altitude where the mesopause is located. Above this height in the atmosphere, the average temperature begins to rise again in the region called the *thermosphere.* As far as we know, the temperature continues to rise at higher and higher altitudes above the mesopause as the earth's atmosphere begins to merge with the sun's atmosphere.

The vertical mean distribution of atmospheric temperature can be explained at least qualitatively by the influences of radiation and convection. Since most of the sun's radiation reaches the earth's surface without absorption, one expects that the lowest zones of the troposphere, in contact with the heat-absorbing surface, will be warmer than the upper layers. The mixing resulting from convection currents will carry heat upwards away from the earth's surface to some maximum level, roughly at the tropopause (see also Chapter 6). The isothermal region and the zone of temperature increase above about 20 km has been associated with the intense absorption of solar ultraviolet radiation by ozone, which has been found from 20-50 km height in rather high concentrations. The maximum in temperature at about 45 km is close to the maximum found in the ozone distribution.

The pressure distribution with altitude up to 50 km is shown in Fig. 3-2. In contrast to the temperature variation, the pressure decreases monotonically with altitude.

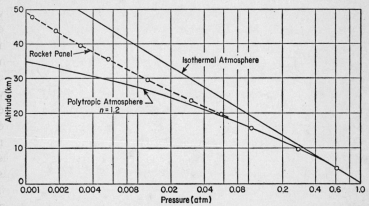

FIG. 3-2 Comparison between the average pressure variation with altitude in the earth's atmosphere and two idealized models [data from "The Rocket Panel," Phys. Rev. 88, 1027-1032 (1952)].

Pressure in Model Atmospheres. Two idealized models of the atmosphere are often used by meteorologists. These ideal cases are:

1. *Isothermal Atmosphere*
   Temperature = constant.
2. *Polytropic Atmosphere*
   p/ρ^n = constant,

where n is a constant greater than unity. If $n = 1$, the polytropic model becomes isothermal. The exponent n gives the atmospheric model an arbitrary parameter to fit observations. Generally, n is found to lie between unity and γ, the ratio of the specific heat of the gas taken at constant pressure and to that at constant volume. For dry air, γ is approximately 1.4. The best value of n to fit the observed distribution of mean pressure in the troposphere is approximately 1.2.

The vertical distribution of hydrostatic pressure can easily be determined for the model atmospheres by integrating the barometric equation, using either condition 1 or condition 2 above. For the isothermal atmosphere,

$$p = p_0 \exp (-g\, \rho_0/p_0)z. \tag{3.4}$$

The coefficient $(g\, \rho_0/p_0)$ is called a reciprocal scale height and has a value of about 0.125 km^{-1} for air. In the case of the polytropic atmosphere, the barometric equation yields:

$$\frac{p}{p_0} = \left[1 - \left(\frac{n-1}{n} \right) \left(\frac{\rho_0}{p_0} \right) g(z - z_0) \right]^{n/(n-1)}. \tag{3.5}$$

In Fig. 3-2 are shown curves for pressure versus altitude calculated for the two models as compared to the observed mean distribution of pressure. Curiously enough the isothermal atmosphere is a good approximation for the actual pressure distribution over the first 6 km altitude even though the atmospheric temperature is not constant. The polytropic model compares well with the observations up to about 18 km when $n = 1.2$.

GETTING VERTICAL MOTION STARTED IN A STATIC ATMOSPHERE

The hydrostatic model of the atmosphere provides an adequate picture of the observed average distribution of properties of the air. However, the really important and the more interesting features of the atmosphere, including its motion, are reflected in the deviations from the average behavior. Some ideas about vertical motion in air can be obtained if we examine what happens when the air at equilibrium is perturbed by a small disturbance. The action of gravity on the disturbed body of fluid may counteract the disturbance or the action may cause the gas to be displaced further from equilibrium, depending on the properties fluid at the location of the disturbance.

Classes of questions whose answers predict a tendency towards amplification or decay of disturbances are called stability problems. Mechanical stability can be divided into two categories: (a) static stability, which is concerned with the initial tendency for motion in a system disturbed from rest, and (b) dynamic stability, which deals with the continued behavior of a moving system. In this section, static stability will be discussed in relation to gravity.

To illustrate the notion of stability of bodies at rest, let us look at what happens to a ball resting in a tank of water as drawn in Fig. 3-3. Suppose the ball is pushed downwards a small distance from its original position z_0 to z_1. If, after the push, the ball gradually rises and returns to rest at its origin, z_0, the system is said to be in *stable equilibrium*. If the ball does not return to z_0, but tends to stop at z_1 after the disturbance, the system is in *neutral equilibrium*. When the ball continues to move downward from z_1 and does not stop, the equilibrium is *unstable*.

The static stability, or the tendency for particles to return to rest or to be accelerated after an initial perturbation, depends on the balance of forces acting on the particle. To determine how bodies such as the ball in Fig. 3-3 react to disturbances, we center attention on the buoyancy force acting on the spherical body.

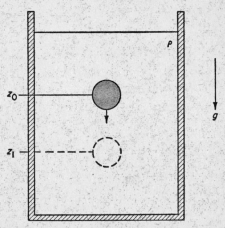

FIG. 3-3 A small vertical displacement of a ball in a tank of fluid.

Suppose we imagine that a portion of the fluid is enclosed by a filmy surface corresponding to the sphere in Fig. 3-3. The vector sum of the external forces acting on the enclosed body must support the sphere, and must equal the weight of the fluid inside the

surface. In other words, the buoyancy force on the submerged
element equals the weight of the fluid it displaces. This statement
is the well known *buoyancy principle* named for Archimedes.
The legend of Archimedes' discovery provides one of the more
amusing stories of scientific achievement. Historically it is not
clear whether Archimedes actually recognized buoyancy or
whether he found only that a solid body displaces its own volume
of fluid. In any case, the story is told that the revelation of the
effect of the buoyancy force fell upon Archimedes in his bath.
He is reputed to have run unclothed from the water shouting,
"Heurēka (I have found it)!"

The Criterion for Static Stability. To obtain a criterion for
static stability, one considers an element of fluid which is displaced a small vertical distance from its original position z_0, where
z is positive upwards. The resultant force on the element is calculated. This will determine whether or not there is a tendency for
the fluid to return to its origin, z_0. Let $\rho_0 g$ represent the weight
per unit volume of the fluid element which is moved, and let
$\rho_1 g$ denote the weight per unit volume of the fluid displaced when
the element is moved to a position z_1. The net force F per unit
volume acting on the element which moves is the difference between the weight of the element and the weight of the displaced
fluid:

$$F = (\rho_0 - \rho_1)g.$$

If we define the stability as

$$S = \lim_{(z_1 - z_0) \to 0} \frac{\rho_0 - \rho_1}{z_1 - z_0} = -\left(\frac{d\rho}{dz}\right), \qquad (3.6)$$

we obtain the following criteria:

$$
\begin{array}{ll}
S > 0 & \text{Stable} \\
S < 0 & \text{Unstable} \\
S = 0 & \text{Neutral.}
\end{array}
$$

When a fluid is layered in such a way that the density decreases
with height, the vertical structure is stable to small disturbances
from rest. However, when the density increases with height, there
is unstable stratification, and vertical motion will begin. A fluid
having no density change with height is neutrally stable to pertur-

bations in the vertical direction. As one might expect, the mean distribution of density as shown in Fig. 3-1 in the atmosphere is a stable configuration.

Disturbances in a Polytropic Atmosphere. The polytropic atmosphere fits the distribution of atmospheric properties in the troposphere. Therefore, some ideas about the initiation of vertical motion should be obtainable by considering conditions of stability in this simple model. To determine the effect of a disturbance in the polytropic atmosphere, the nature of the perturbation has to be specified. Suppose the element is moved vertically without allowing heat to be lost or gained by the element during its displacement. This transition is called an *adiabatic* change. When a perfect gas undergoes an adiabatic disturbance,

$$\frac{p}{\gamma} = \text{constant}, \tag{3.7}$$

where γ is the ratio of specific heats (see p. 37).

To find the criteria for stability in a polytropic atmosphere, we will examine again the relationship between the density of the disturbed element and the density of the fluid it displaces. The symbols p_0 and ρ_0 will indicate the initial equilibrium conditions at z_0 and p^* and ρ^* will represent the conditions of the disturbed element at z_1. The equilibrium pressure and density at z_1 correspond to p_1 and ρ_1, respectively. When the element is moved adiabatically from z_0 to z_1, it is assumed that the gas takes on the equilibrium pressure, $p^* = p_1$. The ratio of densities for an adiabatic disturbance is:

$$\frac{\rho^*}{\rho_0} = \left(\frac{p^*}{p_0}\right)^{1/\gamma} = \left(\frac{p_1}{p_0}\right)^{1/\gamma}. \tag{3.8}$$

In a polytropic atmosphere,

$$\frac{\rho_1}{\rho_0} = \left(\frac{p_1}{p_0}\right)^{1/n} \tag{3.9}$$

or

$$\frac{\rho^*}{\rho_1} = \left(\frac{p_1}{p_0}\right)^{(1/\gamma - 1/n)}. \tag{3.10}$$

Hence, descending elements are stable if $\rho^* < \rho_1$ since $p_1 > p_0$; ascending elements are stable when $\rho^* > \rho_1$ because $p_1 < p_0$. The force acting on a disturbed element depends on $(\rho^* - \rho_1)g$, so let us look at a stability parameter S', which is defined as $(\rho^* - \rho_1)/(z_1 - z_0)$. Using Eqs. (3.10) and (3.6), we can show that

$$S' \approx \rho^* g(\rho_0/p_0)\left(\frac{1}{n} - \frac{1}{\gamma}\right). \qquad (3.11)^2$$

As $(z_1 - z_0)$ becomes small, the ratio $(\rho^* - \rho_1)/(z_1 - z_0)$ approaches $(\rho_0 - \rho_1)/(z_1 - z_0)$, and

$$S \approx \rho^* g\left(\frac{\rho_0}{p_0}\right)\left(\frac{1}{n} - \frac{1}{\gamma}\right) \qquad (3.11A)$$

as $(z_1 - z_0) \to 0$. In terms of Eq. (3.11A) then, the conditions of stability in the polytropic atmosphere are:

$$S > 0 \qquad n < \gamma \qquad \text{Stable}$$
$$S < 0 \qquad n > \gamma \qquad \text{Unstable}$$
$$S = 0 \qquad n = \gamma \qquad \text{Neutral.}$$

Application to the Earth's Atmosphere. Considering the earth's atmosphere as a polytropic model, we find from Eq. (3.11A) and the definition of an adiabatic disturbance in Eq. (3.8) that neutrally stable conditions only exist for adiabatic changes. In this model, it is found that the temperature decreases in dry air at a rate of about 1°C per 100 meters altitude as a result of expansion of the gas. Vertical temperature gradients of this magnitude are actually found under neutral conditions in the earth's atmosphere. Meteorologists call this temperature gradient the *dry adiabatic lapse rate.*

The stability of air masses can be evaluated by comparing measurements of the vertical distribution of temperature with the adiabatic lapse rate. Figure 3-4 shows a hypothetical example of such measurements. The light lines plotted on this temperature-altitude diagram represent neutral equilibrium for the dry adiabatic lapse rate. An idealized set of data taken, for example, by a balloon sounding is shown by the heavy line. Section A of this line denotes a neutrally stable region of the atmosphere $(n = \gamma)$. Section B corresponds to a stable stratification $(n < \gamma)$ while Section C designates an unstable configuration $(n > \gamma)$.

[2] See also Problem 2 at the end of the book.

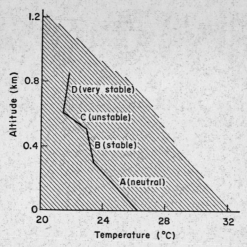

FIG. 3-4 A hypothetical distribution of atmospheric temperature superimposed on lines denoting the dry adiabatic lapse rate.

Section D shows an extremely stable situation where there is an increase in temperature with height. This kind of layering is known as an *inversion*.

When elements of air are set into vertical motion in stably stratified layers, they tend to lose momentum and subside to their original position. Hence, the development of vertical currents is inhibited, suppressing the vertical transport of water vapor, dust, and other minor constituents of the air. In contrast, unstable stratification promotes the amplification of vertical motion. Vertical exchange of moisture increases in cases of unstable layering so that favorable conditions for the development of convective clouds are created (see also Chapter 6).

Water Vapor and Stability. The atmosphere can carry increasing amounts of water vapor as the temperature increases. The concentration of water vapor in air can be defined in terms of the *specific humidity, q*:

$$q = \frac{\text{gm water vapor}}{\text{gm moist air}}. \qquad (3.12)$$

The specific humidity depends on temperature and on the total pressure. Table 3.1 shows some examples of the maximum con-

centration of water vapor which can be found in air in the absence
of condensation.

TABLE 3–1 *Specific Humidity at Saturation Conditions* (q_s). *Total Pressure: 1* atm.

T (°C)	10	15	20	25	30	35	40	45
Specific Humidity $q_s \cdot 100$	0.767	1.07	1.47	2.00	2.69	3.58	4.73	6.18

Another way of measuring the amount of water vapor in air
uses the *relative humidity,* f:

$$f = q/q_s. \qquad (3.13)[3]$$

If the air is saturated, the relative humidity is 100%.

What influence does moisture have on the stability of air? Until
air becomes saturated, water in the vapor phase has very little
effect on ascending air masses. As air expands during rising, the
temperature decreases and the relative humidity increases. If
saturation is reached, condensation may begin on dust or other
nuclei.[4] As the water vapor condenses, heat is given off by release
of the latent heat of vaporization of water. The heat release causes
the rate of temperature decrease with height in cloudy air to be
less than in dry air. In fact, the *moist adiabatic lapse rate* is approximately one-half that of the dry adiabatic lapse rate.

It is possible for an element of rising air to change its stability
with respect to the surroundings if saturation is reached. As an
example, suppose we consider an element being forced upward
through a stable environment as sketched in Fig. 3-5. Initially the
element ascends at the dry adiabatic lapse rate. In this case, the
air is cooling faster than the surrounding air so that it must be
lifted upwards by some mechanical "push" to overcome the
stabilizing forces at these levels. At Point A, the air in the element

[3] By international agreement, f is defined as the observed mixing ratio, w,
divided by the mixing ratio at saturation, w_s. The mixing ratio denotes the
weight of water vapor per unit weight of dry air. The specific humidity q
equals $w/1 + w$). In most cases, $q \approx w$ so that there is no appreciable error
in Eq. (3.13).

[4] See also C. Knight, *The Freezing of Supercooled Liquids,* Momentum
Book No. 14 (D. Van Nostrand Co., Inc., Princeton, New Jersey, 1966), p. 33.

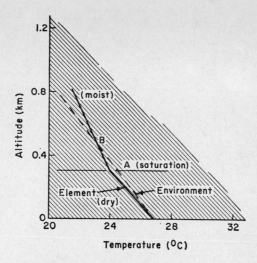

FIG. 3-5 Changes in lapse rate in cloudy air.

reaches saturation, and its ascent proceeds along the moist adiabatic lapse rate. The air in the element remains cooler than the
surroundings so that the mechanical lifting must continue. As
the vapor in the element condenses to form a cloud, the altitude-
temperature curve of the rising mass may eventually cross the
curve for the environment (Point B). In this region, the cloudy
air will become unstable in relation to the surroundings. That is,
the element now cools more slowly than the surrounding air, and
the cloudy air can continue to rise without further mechanical
help.

Vertical Motion—Convection. So far we have examined some
of the implications of disturbances in fluids at rest. The nature
and causes of the initial displacements were not discussed. The relation between movements in the surroundings and the accelera-
tions of fluid elements were also disregarded. The idealized
picture of vertical displacement described above only applies to
changes in the state of individual elements of fluid in surroundings at hydrostatic equilibrium. In reality, the atmosphere never
comes completely to rest. When elements of air flow upwards, the
adjacent fluid must descend. The ensuing convective motion can

change the local distribution of density from the configuration expected from the theory of hydrostatics. The realization of an average distribution of density corresponding to the adiabatic lapse rate ultimately depends on thorough mixing by convection in the atmosphere. Hence, when fluid elements ascend quasi-adiabatically, meeting surroundings at the same temperature as their own at all altitudes, the atmosphere is said to exist in convective equilibrium.

Under conditions where the atmosphere is not in hydrostatic equilibrium, the distributions of density and pressure can take on different configurations. When surfaces of constant density are parallel with surfaces of constant pressure in the air, conditions are said to be *barotropic*. If the surfaces of constant density do not coincide with surfaces of constant pressure, the atmosphere has a *baroclinic* structure.

4 Forces and Motion

KINEMATICS—THE GEOMETRY OF MOTION

The language of fluid dynamics provides the framework for describing and analyzing atmospheric motion. Therefore, it seems useful to outline briefly some important features of the classical theory of fluids before continuing to discuss the behavior of the winds.

Like all areas of theoretical physics, the mechanics of gases have been developed in terms of a concise descriptive structure which are used to analyze quantitatively the behavior of fluid bodies. To begin with, one defines a set of rules about the representation of fluid bodies in motion. These rules constitute *kinematics,* the geometrical description of the movement of bodies without referring to the nature of the forces acting on the bodies.

When an element of fluid travels through space it may stretch out or be pressed together, and it may twist around in different directions. The history of passage of a small element of fluid may be traced schematically along a path as drawn in Fig. 4-1. Suppose a small disk-shaped element at location 1 is identified as if it were enclosed by a completely flexible envelope of plastic. As the disk moves along, it traces out an imaginary tube along its trajectory s, drawn in Fig. 4-1. In traveling from 1 to 2, the disk changes its shape by compression in the vertical plane. While continuing its motion from 2 to 3, the disk rotates about an axis parallel to s as indicated by the twisting trajectories of two points on the disk's surface. From position 3 to 4, the disk displays a change in direction of motion, or it rotates around an axis perpendicular to the

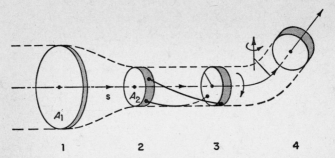

FIG. 4-1   Passage of a disk-like element of fluid along its trajectory in space.

track, s. Similar examples of distortion and twisting of fluid elements also can be visualized by watching filaments of smoke following air motion in a room [Plate VII(A)], or by observing the changes in traces of dye flowing with water in a tank or a transparent pipe.

The passage of fluid elements through a region in space has been formulated geometrically within two different schemes of representation, one originating with Lagrange, and the other with Euler. The Lagrangian method places the frame of reference on a particular fluid element as it travels through space. The Eulerian method centers attention on a train of many fluid elements passing one small region of space at a given instant in time.

Curves in space traced by an individual element such as the one in Fig. 4-1 are called *trajectories* or *particle paths*. In contrast, a curve drawn through each point in space tangent to the fluid velocity vector at that point is called a *streamline*. Streamlines generally bear no relation to particle paths because different fluid elements form different streamlines at given times. However, in cases where the fluid motion is *steady,* i.e., the motion remains the same at each point in space independent of time, streamlines and particle paths are identical. If the fluid element tracing the tube in Fig. 4-1 is in steady motion only, the particle path s then would represent a streamline.

It is often convenient to think of infinitesimal bundles of streamlines as representing a *stream tube*. If the disk in Fig. 4-1 is infinitesimal in cross section, and its flow is steady again, the tube shown in the drawing would correspond to a stream tube.

By definition, no fluid can cross a stream tube's boundaries, and hence the fluid velocity remains constant over the tube's cross-sectional area, which is perpendicular to the direction of streamlines composing the tube.

Continuity. The important principle of conservation of mass, called *continuity* in fluid mechanics, also can be illustrated using the stream tube of Fig. 4-1. Continuity requires that a steadily flowing mass of fluid passing into a given volume must be the same as the mass coming out. The amount of fluid entering the stream tube at 1 is given by the product of the fluid density ρ_1, the velocity q_1, and the cross-sectional area A_1, which is normal to the streamlines. The mass of fluid leaving at 2 is $\rho_2 q_2 A_2$. Satisfying the principle of continuity,

$$\rho_1 q_1 A_1 = \rho_2 q_2 A_2. \qquad (4.1)$$

When variations in density are negligible, continuity is maintained by balancing the product of the fluid velocity and the area through which the fluid flows. This principle may be used to explain the origins of unusually strong winds between tall buildings. If a steady wind forces air of constant density from a region of relatively wide cross-section into a very narrow street lined with buildings, the air flow along the narrow passage must increase to compensate for the constriction of area, and thus a much stronger wind will be induced in the constricted zone. Like many people, I frequently have encountered such increases in wind in the comparatively narrow streets of New York City as icy-cold gusts of wind blow east through the City from the Hudson River during the winter.

Considering the increase in motion through city streets, or the steady flow from 1 to 2 in the tube of Fig. 4-1, we see how streamlines may be pressed together with a reduction in area. The forcing together of streamlines, or the parting of streamlines involves the sideways approach of fluid elements to one another. These changes are called respectively *confluence* and *diffluence* [Fig. 4-2(A)]. On the other hand, fluid elements may be pressed together or separated along the direction of motion, causing an accumulation or a decrease in fluid mass in a particular volume of space. These effects are called respectively *convergence* and

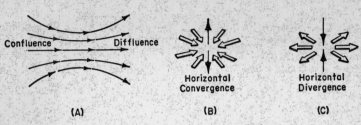

Confluence   Diffluence

Horizontal
Convergence

Horizontal
Divergence

(A)   (B)   (C)

FIG. 4-2   Illustration of meaning of several terms.

divergence. If there is a converging, constant-density flow horizontally towards a region, continuity requires that a compensating vertical flow out from this region, as drawn in Fig. 4-2(B). Similarly, as indicated in Fig. 4-2(C), horizontally diverging flow at constant density must involve a vertical inflow to satisfy continuity.

The atmosphere is bounded at the bottom by the earth's surface and at the top by an ill-defined upper level at high altitude. Because the net vertical velocity of air must be effectively zero at these boundaries, the presence of any local vertical motion requires that horizontal convergence or divergence must take place above and below. A region of steady upward flow, for example, is maintained by convergence at low levels and divergence at upper levels; i.e., by outward winds at high altitude, and inward winds at low altitude. Similarly, a steady downward flow requires divergence below, and convergence above.

Deformation and Rotation in a Fluid Element. So far we have looked at some features of fluid flow in translation, and of the interplay between different fluid particles. Now let us consider how changes of shape, size, and rotation affect the same fluid element. Differences in shape or size can come about as a fluid element deforms, while the rotation of an element changes its orientation in space. A combination of these two effects covers all of the geometrical alterations that a particular fluid element may experience.

The geometry of deformation and rotation can be seen by considering modifications in the cubical element of fluid in Fig. 4-3. Suppose the element is pushed out of shape by a pair of forces

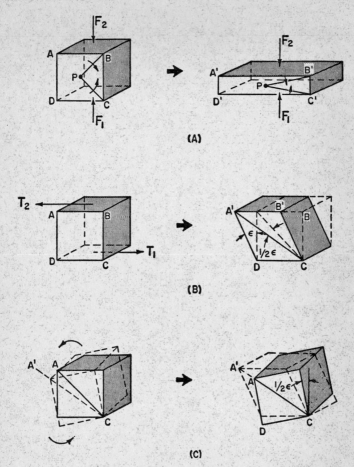

FIG. 4-3 Distortion of a fluid element.

acting perpendicularly to the horizontal faces of the cube [Fig. 4-3(A)]. This corresponds to the change in shape of the disk as it experiences forces acting radially in the vertical plane while traversing from 1 to 2 in Fig. 4-1. After deformation, the face of the cube ABCD changes to rectangular shape A'B'C'D'. As the cube deforms, lines like AB and BD do not rotate, but lines like PB and PD do. Nevertheless, the total rotation as measured by the addition of the angular velocities of lines PB and PD remains zero. That is, the angular velocity of PB is equal in magnitude to that of PD, but their directions of rotation are opposed, hence there is no net rotation.

On the other hand, suppose the cube is subjected to a pair of shearing forces acting parallel to the horizontal faces as indicated in Fig. 4-3(B). The cube will be pushed by these forces into the shape of a parallelepiped shown by the solid lines in Fig. 4-3(B). If the angle that the deformed edge A′D makes with the original edge AD is ϵ, then the diagonal A′C has moved through $\epsilon/2$ since A′C bisects the angle DCB′ just as AC originally bisected the right angle DCB. Now suppose that the original cube is rotated without change in shape by $\epsilon/2$, so that AC coincides with A′C as indicated in Fig. 4-3(C). Then the true net deformation of the element must be the difference between the deformed body in Fig. 4-3(B), and the rotated cube shown together in Fig. 4-3(C). Hence, the net deformation is less than that shown in Fig. 4-3(B). If the rotation of the originally perpendicular lines DC (zero rotation) and A′D (ϵ rotation) are added, and are divided by two, the net rotation of the body is $\epsilon/2$, in agreement with the above geometrical argument.

The sum of the rates of rotation of a pair of lines like PB and PD, or DC and A′D in Fig. 4-3 is called the *vorticity* in the plane of the two lines. When the vorticity equals zero, there is deformation without rotation as shown in Fig. 4-3(A). Finite vorticity expresses the pure rotation occurring in a deforming body as indicated in Figs. 4-3(B) or 4-3(C).

Sections 2 to 3, and 3 to 4 in Fig. 4-1 show how vorticity can be present in a translating element of fluid along two different axes of rotation. The magnitude of the vorticity in the rotation of the disk from 2 to 3 can be estimated, for example, by applying the ideas developed for the cube in Fig. 4-3. At 2, suppose the fluid disk rotates as a rigid body with an angular velocity Ω about the axis of rotation s and that the coordinates x and y form the plane perpendicular to s as indicated in Fig. 4-4. The disk's tangential velocity at radius r equals $r\Omega$ [Fig. 4-4(A)]. Looking directly at the rotating plane in the s direction, Fig. 4-4(B), we can draw at point B a triangle whose sides are proportional to the

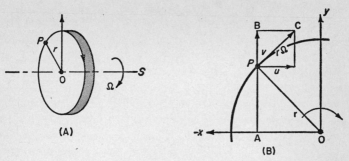

FIG. 4-4   A disk of fluid rotating as a solid body.

components of the tangential velocity vector $r\Omega$. Since the triangles PAO and CBP are similar,

$$\frac{u}{y} = \frac{r\Omega}{r} = \frac{v}{-x},$$

or

$$u = y\Omega, \qquad v = -x\Omega. \tag{4.2}$$

Considering the limit of infinitesimal changes in the velocity components u and v in the y and x directions only, written as $\partial u/\partial y$ and $\partial v/\partial x$, an equality of ratios follows from Eq. (4.2):

$$\frac{\partial u}{\partial y} = -\frac{\partial v}{\partial x} = \Omega. \tag{4.3}$$

The average rotation of the point P around O for infinitesimal velocity changes in the xy plane is found by taking the mean of the sum of the two expressions for the angular velocity Ω:

$$\text{average rotation in the } xy \text{ plane} = R_{xy} = \frac{1}{2}\left(\frac{\partial u}{\partial y} - \frac{\partial v}{\partial x}\right). \tag{4.4}$$

This expression represents half the value of the vorticity associated with the rotation of the disk in the xy plane. In general, there are two other components of vorticity, one in the xz plane, and one in the zy plane. The three components of vorticity give the spin of a fluid element an orientation in space as well as a size scale. Hence vorticity is denoted in mathematical shorthand by a vector parallel to the axis of net rotation of the fluid element, and proportional to the net angular velocity of the element. The vorticity vector is positively directed in the sense of the advance of a right-handed screw. In the case shown in Fig. 4-4(B), the vorticity is positive for R_{xy} when the coordinate $-x$ rotates towards y through the smaller of the angles between them.

Vortex Lines and Tubes. Vorticity often is traced in a fluid body by *vortex lines.* In analogy to the streamline, a vortex line consists of a line that is tangent to the local axis of rotation, the vorticity vector, at each point along the line. Vortex tubes or filaments represent infinitesimal bundles of vortex lines. Crudely speaking, a tornado or a waterspout may be considered a giant sized vortex tube (Plate VI).

The vorticity in a vortex tube sometimes is defined in terms of *circulation,* a quantity proportional to the total amount of vorticity intersecting a surface. The circulation Γ around the circular disk of radius r in Fig. 4-4, representing a fluid rotating as a solid, equals the tangential velocity times the length of the disk's circumference, $2\pi r^2 \Omega$. But the vorticity in the plane of the disk is 2Ω so that the circulation becomes the area of the circle times the total vorticity. Generalizing to a surface of arbitrary shape, the circulation around a closed curve or boundary equals the flux of vorticity through the plane of the closed curve. This theorem, found by Helmholtz, implies that the flux of vorticity, *the strength of a vortex tube,* remains constant at all points along the tube. This in turn requires that a vortex tube cannot end in the fluid, but it can form into a closed ring.

Changes in Vorticity. As fluid elements move through space, their vorticity can change. Variation in existing vorticity occurs through the shifting of the components of vorticity by turning vortex lines, or by the stretching of vortex lines. Generation of vorticity in a fluid element comes about by the action of frictional forces and buoyancy forces, as we shall see later.

Changes in components of vorticity during the turning of vortex lines will be illustrated below when we consider the forces on fluids that result from differences in pressure. To demonstrate how the stretching or compressing of vortex lines affects the vorticity, let us consider what happens to a tiny rotating cylindrical element as it passes through a section like region 1 to 2 in the "tube" of Fig. 4-1. As sketched in Fig. 4-5, the cylinder of con-stand density fluid of radius r_1 and length L_1, rotating at an angu-lar speed of Ω_1 has associated with it a vortex line which displays

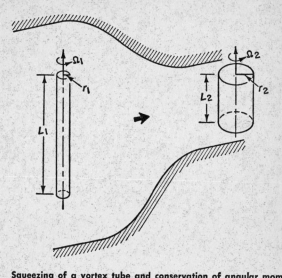

FIG. 4-5 Squeezing of a vortex tube and conservation of angular momentum.

the axis of the element's rotation. The cylinder is oriented in such a way that it is compressed along the direction of its axis of rota-tion (the vortex line) as it moves through the region of con-fluence. If the mass m of the element remains constant, the radius r_2 after the confluence equals $r_1(L_1/L_2)^{1/2}$. The moment of inertia of the element at 1, I_1, changes from $mr_1^2/2$ to $I_2 = (mr_1^2/2) (L_1/L_2)$. If the element is in rigid body rotation, the angular momentum M remains the same from 1 to 2, so that

$$M = I_1\Omega_1 = I_2\Omega_2,$$

or

$$\Omega_2 = (I_1/I_2)\Omega_1 = (L_2/L_1)\Omega_1. \tag{4.5}$$

Since the vorticity is proportional to the local angular velocity in the fluid, the vorticity then must decrease by the compression as a consequence of the tendency to conserve angular momentum.

The behavior of a rotating element of fluid during stretching or shrinking is analogous to the changes of rotational velocity of a skater in a spin. Using the principle of conservation of angular momentum, for example, a skater who is spinning with his arms at his body may decrease his rate of spin by outstretching his arms. In spreading his arms, the skater increases his moment of inertia, and causes a decrease in his angular velocity as indicated by Eq. (4.5).

BODY FORCE AND STRATIFIED FLUIDS

To set a body of fluid in motion, unbalanced forces must act on that body. The forces affecting fluid motion fall into two classes: *body forces,* which act upon the mass of the fluid element, and *surface forces,* which act on the surface of a fluid element.

Gravity. The most common body force acting on the atmosphere is the gravitational force. The true Newtonian gravitational attraction of the earth is directed towards the center of mass of the planet. This force is inversely proportional to the square of the distance between the center of the earth and an element of the atmosphere. However, the gravitational force that actually has been measured on the earth, called *gravity,* includes a very small, but noticeable centrifugal effect of the earth's rotation. We can see how the rotating planet's influence on the measured gravitational force comes about by considering the balance of forces on an air particle of unit mass, which is at rest with respect to the earth's surface. The particle is located at point P, at latitude θ, as drawn in Fig. 4-6. The perpendicular distance from the axis of rotation to P is R, and the distance from P to the earth's center of mass M, is r. Since the planet rotates at an angular velocity of Ω, an air particle at rest with respect to the earth must rotate at the same speed. Part of the true gravitational force g_N, directed along $\mathbf{r}$ towards M supplies the centripetal force $\mathbf{F}_c$, of magnitude $\Omega^2 R$, directed inwards along R towards the axis of rotation. The apparent gravitational force $\mathbf{g}$ then equals the vector sum:

$$\mathbf{g} = \mathbf{g}_N + \mathbf{F}_c. \qquad (4.6)$$

From the vector diagram in Fig. 4-6, we see that the observed acceleration due to gravity depends on the latitude angle, or varies from equator to pole, and is directed towards a point inside the

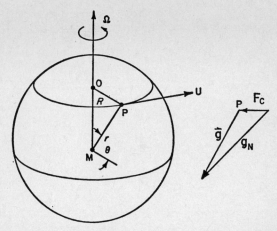

FIG. 4-6 The spinning earth and the vector representing gravity.

earth which differs slightly from the center of mass M. The centripetal effect in gravity causes a variation of 0.5% in the magnitude of **g** from 0° to 90° latitude. The variation in gravity with altitude up to 30 km, according to the inverse square proportionality of distance, amounts to about 1%. Therefore, the vector representing gravity is assumed to be directed perpendicular to the earth's horizon, and as a first approximation, to be constant in magnitude, equal to 9.80 meters sec^{-2}.

Vorticity Generation by Density Differences. Aside from keeping the earth's atmosphere in place, the action of gravity plays an indispensable role in maintaining the vertical component of atmospheric motion. Gravity also contributes to the generation of rotational motion in stratified air. As we found in Chapter 3, lighter air under heavier air will tend to rise upwards to a more stable region. Such a movement of buoyant fluid must be accompanied by a compensating downward flow of heavier fluid around the rising body of air. Thus, during overturning, a rotation of air develops in a vertical plane which takes the appearance of a vortex ring, sketched in Fig. 4-7.

The generation of vorticity resulting from density variations in fluids can be calculated in terms of the circulation Γ. Induction of circulation around a closed curve, always encompassing the same fluid elements, can occur with the action of buoyancy forces,

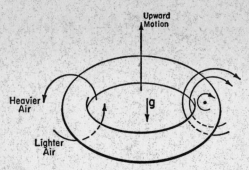

FIG. 4-7   Circulation of buoyant fluid in a vortex ring. [After R. S. Scorer, *Natural Aerodynamics* (Pergamon Press, New York, 1958), p. 66.]

or under the influence of friction. In the case of a frictionless, stratified fluid in a non-rotating system of coordinates, V. Bjerknes demonstrated many years ago that rate of change in circulation with time is related to the distribution of lines of constant pressure and constant density in a body of air by the expression:

(Baroclinic) $$\frac{d\Gamma}{dt} = -\int_C \frac{dp}{\rho}.$$ (4.7)

The right side of Eq. (4.7) denotes the sum of all the values of the ratio of pressure to density around an arbitrary closed curve of circumference C in a baroclinic fluid. If the fluid is barotropic, Eq. (4.7) reduces to another important relation found by Lord Kelvin:

(Barotropic) $$\frac{d\Gamma}{dt} = 0.$$ (4.8)

Since the derivative on the left side of Eq. (4.8) represents the change in Γ with time, always following the same fluid element, Kelvin's relation tells us that the circulation, and consequently the vorticity, remains constant within an element of frictionless, barotropic fluid.

PRESSURE GRADIENT FORCES IN BAROTROPIC FLOW

Although gravity acts only in the vertical direction on fluid bodies, surface forces may exert their influence on fluids in any

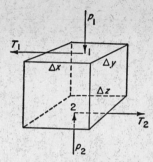

FIG. 4-8 Surface forces acting on a cube of fluid.

direction. Surface forces per unit area are called *stresses*, and may be divided as indicated in Fig. 4-8 into normal components (pressure) and tangential components (shearing stresses). The shearing stress involves friction between adjacent layers of fluid. Roughly speaking, pressure differences cause changes in the volume of a fluid body while the action of shearing stresses imparts a change in shape of a fluid body.

When an element of fluid remains in equilibrium with its surroundings, the sum of the forces acting on the element is zero. Experimental observations have indicated that the surface forces are perpendicular to all immersed surfaces of a body at rest, or in hydrostatic equilibrium. Also at equilibrium, the pressure at a point in the fluid is found to be equal in all directions. That is, the pressure has no preferred direction of action, and thus it can be represented by a magnitude only (a scalar quantity).

Differences in Pressure. In the absence of friction and body forces, fluid elements can be accelerated only if a difference in pressure exists between two points in the fluid. The acceleration of a cubical fluid element resulting from a pressure difference can be estimated easily. Suppose that the normal stresses act only on the horizontal planes of a cube, as indicated in Fig. 4-8. When the pair of tangential components is zero, or is balanced, the cubical element will accelerate in the vertical direction z only if the pressure p_1 at point 1 is not the same as the pressure p_2 at point 2. Taking the dimensions of the cube as infinitesimal lengths Δx, Δy, and Δz $(= z_2 - z_1)$, the force acting on the cube pushing on the xy sides is:

$$F_z = (p_1 - p_2) \, \Delta x \, \Delta y.$$

When the cube accelerates only in the z direction, the pressure
acting on any two parallel sides that are also parallel to z must
be the same. Hence, the net force on the cube, the product of the
mass of the fluid element and its acceleration, equals the force
acting on the horizontal sides of the body, or, for a cube of density
ρ, having velocity w in the z direction,

$$\rho \, \Delta x \, \Delta y \, \Delta z \, \frac{dw}{dt} = (p_1 - p_2) \, \Delta x \, \Delta y.$$

After dividing both sides of this expression by $\Delta x \, \Delta y$, and taking
the limit as Δz approaches zero, we find that

$$\lim_{\Delta z \to 0} \rho \, \frac{dw}{dt} = -\left(\frac{dp}{dz}\right). \tag{4.9}$$

The ratio of the change in pressure dp to a corresponding change
in length dz is called the *gradient of pressure* in the z direction.
The minus sign for the pressure gradient means that the fluid
element has a positive acceleration when it moves from a region
of higher pressure towards a region of lower pressure.

Like acceleration, velocity, and vorticity, the pressure gradient
has both magnitude and direction. Thus, the pressure at a point
is not a vector, but the pressure gradient is a vector. In general
the acceleration of a fluid element takes place in a direction specified by all three coordinates x, y, and z. Hence, in the absence of
the action of other forces, each component of a fluid element's
acceleration must balance the pressure gradient in that direction

$$a_x = -\frac{1}{\rho}\left(\frac{\partial p}{\partial x}\right), \quad a_y = -\frac{1}{\rho}\left(\frac{\partial p}{\partial y}\right), \quad a_z = -\frac{1}{\rho}\left(\frac{\partial p}{\partial z}\right), \tag{4.10}$$

or, in vector notation,

$$\mathbf{a} = a_x\mathbf{i} + a_y\mathbf{j} + a_z\mathbf{k} = -\frac{1}{\rho}\,\text{grad}\,p$$

$$= -\frac{1}{\rho}\left[\left(\frac{\partial p}{\partial x}\right)\mathbf{i} + \left(\frac{\partial p}{\partial y}\right)\mathbf{j} + \left(\frac{\partial p}{\partial z}\right)\mathbf{k}\right], \tag{4.11}$$

where **i**, **j**, and **k** respectively denote unit vectors in the x, y and
z directions. Just as we wrote in Eq. (4.9), Eq. (4.11) indicates

mathematically that the fluid element accelerates in the direction opposite to that of the pressure gradient.

Flow Along a Streamline. It frequently is necessary to know how the pressure is related to the fluid velocity along a streamline. This relation can be calculated for a frictionless fluid in steady flow using a force balance like Eq. (4.9). Suppose we consider an infinitesimal length ds of a stream tube whose cross-section is a constant, A. To be perfectly general, the section of stream tube is drawn in Fig. 4-9 so that it is inclined at an angle ϕ to the

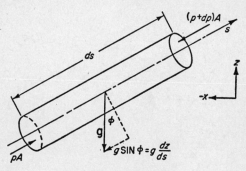

FIG. 4-9 A stream tube.

vertical direction z. The surface force acting on the left face is p times A. The surface force acting on the right face is $(p + dp)A$. To write the balance of forces along the direction of s, a component of gravity has to be taken into account also. The total body force acting on the volume $A\,ds$ is $\rho g A\,ds$. However, its component along s is given by $\rho g A\,ds \sin \phi$. Balancing the pressure forces and the body force component with the acceleration of the fluid along s, and noting that $\sin \phi = dz/ds$, we find that

$$\rho A\,ds \left(\frac{dq}{dt}\right) = A[p - (p + dp)] - \rho A\,ds\,g\,\frac{dz}{ds}. \tag{4.12}$$

Remembering that ds/dt is the fluid velocity q along s, and that $dq = d(q^2/2)$,

$$d\left(\frac{q^2}{2}\right) + \frac{dp}{\rho} + g\,dz = 0 \tag{4.13}$$

along the infinitesimal section of stream tube. Since no cross-sectional area is involved in Eq. (4.13), this expression applies

also to steady flow along an infinitesimal piece of a streamline
When the fluid density depends on the pressure only (barotrop
ism), Eq. (4.13) may be summed or integrated over a particula
streamline, giving:

$$\frac{q^2}{2} + \int_s \frac{dp}{\rho} + gz = F(x,y,z). \qquad (4.14)$$

Thus in steady flow, the sum of the pressure, the square of the
fluid velocity, and the gravitational potential gz equals the same
arbitrary function along the same streamline. Equation (4.14) i
a form of an important expression discovered by Daniel Bernoull
in 1738.

Bernoulli's equation may be applied to the behavior of a pito
tube to see how this instrument gives a reading of velocity. Th
pitot tube is sketched with streamlines of incoming flow in Fig
2-3. The "central" streamline is represented by line AB. Change
in the vertical direction are disregarded, and the flow is assumed
barotropic. Thus, for the central streamline,

$$\frac{q_A^2}{2} + \frac{p_A}{\rho} = F(x,y,z).$$

At the tip of the pitot tube, point B, called the *stagnation poin*
the velocity of the fluid must be zero, since there can be no flo
inside the tube. Thus from Bernoulli's equation, the *stagnatio*
pressure p_B is:

$$p_B = F(x,y,z).$$

The fluid velocity measured by the instrument is given ideally b
the half power of the difference between the stagnation (static
pressure p_B, and the total pressure p_A:

$$q_A = \left[\frac{2}{\rho} (p_B - p_A) \right]^{1/2}. \qquad (4.15$$

Pressure Differences Across Streamlines. Although the Bernoul
equation tells us about the relation between velocity and pressur

[1] Mathematically, the integration in a particular direction of a proper
that varies spatially involves an arbitrary function instead of a constant. Whe
the flow along a streamline is irrotational, it can be shown that $F(x,y,z) = co$
stant.

long a streamline, it does not indicate what happens across treamlines. To find the pressure variation across streamlines, we ave to integrate the equation of motion along a direction **n**, erpendicular to the direction of streamlines, **s**. When the influ- nce of forces other than the pressure-gradient force is small on a teadily flowing fluid of constant density, the pressure-gradient orce per unit mass will balance the centripetal force per unit nass, which acts perpendicular to curved streamlines. Thus, if he radius of curvature of streamlines is r, the gradient of pressure n the **n** direction then equals the centripetal component or:

$$\frac{\partial p}{\partial n} = \frac{\rho q^2}{r}. \tag{4.16}$$

Note that the centripetal force acting on a fluid tends to result n a flow perpendicular to the pressure gradient instead of parallel o the pressure gradient. This relation indicates that the pressure ises in passage from the concave side of a curved streamline to he convex side by an amount $\rho q^2/r$ per unit length. Then, as → ∞, we note that no difference in pressure can exist in a direc- on transverse to the direction of flow. Equation (4.16) essentially efines the *cyclostrophic wind*, a flow curving around a circular ath.

Pressure Gradient Influencing Vorticity. With the aid of Eqs. 1.14) and (4.16) we can see how the pressure gradient affects the orticity in a fluid. As an example, suppose a fluid of constant ensity flows steadily around a bend of constant cross-section like ec. 3 to 4 of the tube in Fig. 4-1. The movement of a row of fluid articles as they pass around the bend of the tube is viewed from bove as sketched in Fig. 4-10. In the absence of rotation at 3, the articles near the inside curve of the bend move faster than the articles at the outside of the bend as a consequence of Ber- oulli's relation combined with the cyclostrophic effect. Hence ie line of fluid particles is stretched out and turned as shown at cation 4. Now if the fluid possesses vorticity, the vortex lines can e drawn in with the fluid particles as indicated in Fig. 4-10. Thus orticity orginally oriented such that its axis of rotation parallel o the row of particles at 3 is changed in magnitude, and re- iented in the flow through the bend to 4. Since the vortex lines

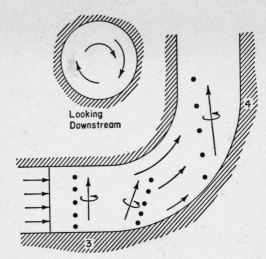

Looking
Downstream

FIG. 4-10 Flow in the bend of a channel. [After R. S. Scorer, *Natural Aerodynamics* (Pergamon Press, New York, 1958), p. 79.]

in this case are turned from a direction across the flow towards
direction parallel to flow in the tube at 4, a secondary circulation
pattern following the rotation around the vortex lines may develop as drawn in the inset, Fig. 4-10.

Pressure differences may also contribute to the generation o
vorticity in regions where there are sudden changes in velocity
Virtual discontinuities in velocity often can develop in flowin
fluids. A typical case is sketched in Fig. 4-11(A).

The flow along surfaces of discontinuity in velocity is inher-
ently unstable. Since small disturbances in the motion are ampl
fied in these zones, "sheets" of vortices or eddies develop along th
discontinuity. Early in this century, Ludwig Prandtl gave a simpl
explanation for the generation of vorticity in these situation
Prandtl suggested that the perturbations in flow would caus
waves to form on the surface of discontinuity as indicated in Fi
4-11(B). The waves will propagate at a velocity equal to th
average speed of the two streams. Thus, if a line of reference mo
ing at the wave speed is chosen, the two streams become the o
posing flows shown in Fig. 4-11(B). In general, the function F i

Bernoulli's equation will not be the same for the two "uniform" streams 1 and 2. However, when we refer the motion to the velocity of the waves on the discontinuity, the Bernoulli functions

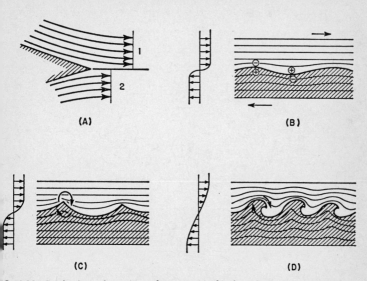

(A)   (B)

(C)   (D)

FIG. 4-11 Production of vortices along an idealized surface of discontinuity in velocity. [After L. Prandtl, *Fuhrer durch die Stromungslehre* (Freidr. Vieweg and Son, Braunschweig, 1949).]

will be equal initially for 1 and 2 even if the velocities of the two streams are opposed. Prandtl then reasoned from the Bernoulli equation and Eq. (4.16) that, for initially steady motion, there will be a tendency to develop an excess pressure at the crest of waves, and a reduced pressure in the troughs, shown by plus and minus signs in Fig. 4-11(B). As the motion becomes unsteady along the discontinuity under the action of infinitesimal pressure gradients, the fluid will move towards the regions of lower pressure. The waves will become more pronounced [Fig. 4-11(C)] until they begin to roll over in the same way ocean waves break on a beach. The rolling up of the surface of discontinuity, as indicated in Fig. 4-11(D), gives rise to a thin layer of eddies which are superimposed on the streamline flow.

THE FRICTIONAL FORCE

When the tangential stresses caused by the influence of frictio
are present, the net action of surface forces becomes more compl
cated. When the pairs of stresses p_1 and p_2 are not equal, an
T_1 and T_2 are not the same on the cube in Fig. 4-8, this body wi
accelerate in a direction that depends on the vector sum of th
pressure gradient force and the frictional force.

The effect of the tangential stresses on the cubical element b
tween two parallel plates is drawn in Fig. 4-12(A). If the enc

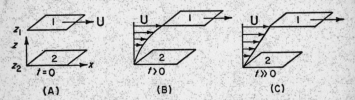

FIG. 4-12 Development of shearing flow between two plates originally at res

and sides are left open, no pressure differences will exist on th
vertical planes of the cube. Thus, when the top plate is set in mo
tion, relative to the bottom plate, only a tangential, friction
stress acts on the cube as indicated schematically in Fig. 4-8. B
cause the fluid sticks to the plates, the top layers of fluid ar
dragged along with the top plate, while the lower layers remai
nearly at rest [Fig. 4-12(B)]. Eventually, a steady flow will develo
as drawn in Fig. 4-12(C) such that the layers close to the plate
move at almost the same velocity as the plates, and the layers i
the middle will adjust their speeds u to be proportional to th
distance $z_2 - z_1$. The friction in the fluid produces a shearin
stress τ_{zx} resisting the movement of the top plate, which is equa
and opposite in direction to the tangential stress exerted by th
plate on the fluid. For many fluids like air and water, the stre
τ_{zx} is proportional to the shear, the coefficient of proportionali
being the fluid viscosity μ. In the limit as the velocity differenc
becomes very small over an infinitesimal difference in z,

$$\tau_{zx} = \lim_{\Delta z \to 0} \mu \left(\frac{u_1 - u_2}{z_2 - z_1} \right) = -\mu \frac{du}{dz}. \qquad (4.1$$

The derivative on the right side of this equation represents the ate of deformation along the xy plane in the x direction.

When the shearing stress in the fluid is equal but opposite in irection in adjacent layers, no net force is exerted between layers. This condition corresponds to the case where the gradient in elocity is constant, as sketched in Fig. 4-12(C). On the other hand, when the velocity gradient is curved a net frictional force acts on he fluid. In a situation like Fig. 4-12(B), the shearing stress increases upwards so that a force is acting on the fluid in the direction to the right. The net frictional force $\mathbf{T}$ per unit mass then depends on the rate of change in shear, and for the case in Fig. -10(B), $\mathbf{T}$ has only one component:

$$T_x = \frac{1}{\rho}\frac{d\tau_{zx}}{dz} = \frac{1}{\rho}\frac{d}{dz}\left(-\mu\,\frac{du}{dz}\right). \tag{4.18}$$

When the fluid velocity also varies in the x and y directions, two more parts will depend on the velocity gradient in the x and y directions, and thus these will contribute to the component T_x. This means that conceivably there may be a total of nine components of the stress involving spatial gradients of the fluid velocity vector.

When the frictional force acts on a fluid particle, it gives rise to a net acceleration in a direction other than the direction of the pressure gradient. Since friction depends on the gradient in fluid velocity, the effect of the frictional force is strongest in regions of large velocity gradients. Usually the change in velocity with altitude nearest the earth's surface is relatively large because the air velocity must be reduced to zero at the boundary. Therefore the frictional force often exerts its strongest influence on the atmosphere near the ground. Thus at high altitudes air tends to move without the influence of friction, while friction plays a more dominant role in air flow nearest to the earth's surface.

The region close to the earth where the gradient in wind velocity is large is called the surface layer, or the *boundary layer*. Although the boundary layers may be defined in several ways, perhaps the simplest definition refers to the region in which 99% of the change in horizontal air speed occurs. The effects of friction, of course, are confined primarily to this layer.

The development of the original theory for fluid flow in bound
ary layers largely is attributed to Ludwig Prandtl and his co
leagues. Because of the importance of the concept of boundar
layers to aerodynamics and to other fields of technology, ther
has been a great deal of research undertaken in this area of flui
dynamics.

Frictional Dissipation and Vorticity Diffusion. The action c
frictional forces on a fluid element tends to convert regular, d
rected translational motion of the element into the irregula
thermal motion of the fluid molecules in the element. The fri
tional force is nonconservative in that it acts to remove kineti
energy of motion from a system. Furthermore, friction is dissip
tive in that it acts to damp out fluid motion as it transfers energ
from the flow to the random motion of fluid molecules. Thu
for example, the action of friction on fluid near the discontinuit
in velocity of Fig. 4-11 would tend to dampen the unstabilizin
effect of pressure. Ordinarily the action of the fluid acceleratio
(the inertial force) and the pressure gradient force are sufficientl
strong in regions of velocity discontinuity to overpower the fri
tional damping, so that eddies tend to form even in cases whei
the difference in velocity between the two streams is quite smal

As a non-conservative force, friction plays the part of a diffuse
of vorticity. The role of viscosity then is to conduct vorticity i
such a way as to smooth out velocity gradients in the same manne
that the thermal conductivity diffuses heat in a body so tha
differences in temperature are leveled out.

Because friction tends to transport vorticity, discontinuities i
velocity like the one in Fig. 4-11 are continuously smoothed ou
Thus, the initially very thin region of large shear, and very larg
vorticity, become thicker and thicker as the frictional forces a
to disperse the rotating motion outward into the fluid in th
neighborhood of the region of velocity difference.

As fluid begins to flow without rotation over a solid surface,
region of strong shear forms at the boundary, which is analogou
to the discontinuity in velocity of Fig. 4-11. As rotation of flui
particles is induced in the zone of large velocity gradients near th
surface, vorticity is generated. The vorticity then tends to diffu:

outward into non-rotating regions of flow under the action of friction. Qualitatively, the layer which grows in thickness as the influence of rotation spreads outwards then can be defined as a boundary layer. This definition, of course, is precisely the same as the one we introduced previously. For further discussion of the behavior of boundary layers, see pp. 116-119.

THE CORIOLIS FORCE

As soon as a particle of air begins to move over the earth's surface, its path will be influenced by an apparent force arising from observations of the particle taken from the rotating planet. Thus, in a coordinate system rotating with respect to frame of reference fixed at the center of the sun (Newton's inertial system), an air particle experiences an effective force made up of the forces listed previously and an additional component associated with the particle's spinning motion relative to the earth. Thus, for example, if an air particle travels with an eastward component of velocity faster than an identical particle sitting on the earth, the air particle will feel an apparent force directed outward along the line perpendicular to the earth's axis of rotation. This force can be resolved into two components, one vertical and one horizontal. The vertical component serves only to change the apparent value of g_N slightly and so is relatively unimportant. On the other hand, the horizontal component is directed southward and, unless compensated for, will cause the eastward-moving particle to accelerate toward the equator. The resulting acceleration is known as the Coriolis acceleration and the part of the force responsible for it is known as the Coriolis force.

When an air particle moves westward relative to the earth, the apparent centrifugal force on it is less than that on an identical particle moving with the earth. Hence it will be accelerated toward the pole.

To find a quantitative relation for the effect of the rotating earth, let us consider a particle P of unit mass, indicated for example in Fig. 4-6. The air particle now travels eastward at a speed u relative to the earth, while an identical particle at rest on the earth has a tangential speed, $U = \Omega R$. The part of the force on P acting in the plane of the horizon and resulting from spinning around the earth's axis depends on the total speed of the particle $(U + u)$. This component is directed towards the equator, and equals.

$$\frac{(U + u)^2 \sin \theta}{R} = \frac{U^2 \sin \theta}{R} + \frac{2Uu \sin \theta}{R} + \frac{u^2 \sin \theta}{R}, \quad (4.19)$$

where θ is the angle of latitude.

The first term on the right side of Eq. (4.19) represents the centripetal force on the particle of unit mass which is at rest with respect to the earth. This component is exactly equal in magnitude and direction to the force $\mathbf{F}_c$ of Eq. (4.6), hence it merely accounts for the difference between $\mathbf{g}$ and $\mathbf{g}_N$ in that equation. The second term in Eq. (4.19) is the deflecting force, the *Coriolis force*, acting on the air particle P moving eastward relative to the identical particle resting on the earth. The third term is normally quite small unless the air particle moves relative to the earth nearly as fast as the planet's tangential speed.

The horizontal component of the Coriolis force per unit mass normally is written as:

$$C_h = \frac{2\Omega R \sin \theta u}{R} = (2\Omega \sin \theta)u = fu, \quad (4.20)$$

where $f = 2\Omega \sin \theta$ is called the Coriolis parameter.

The apparent deflecting force of rotation acting on a westward moving particle has the magnitude given in Eq. (4.20), but this force is directed poleward instead of equatorward as it would be for a particle moving eastward.

Using the principle of conservation of angular momentum, it is possible to show that the Coriolis force acts in the same way on particles flowing in the north-south direction. When an air particle moves towards the equator, the particle will tend to have the same angular momentum as it would if the particle had remained at rest relative to the earth at the latitude where it began its movement. Since particles in the lower latitudes are farther away from the earth's axis of rotation, they have to move at higher tangential speeds to remain at rest relative to the earth. Therefore the particle traveling equatorward from the higher latitude will possess less angular momentum than an identical particle at the lower latitude sitting at rest relative to the earth. Hence the particle traveling from the higher latitudes towards the lower latitudes will lag to the westward. Similarly, a particle moving poleward will travel into regions of smaller radius of curvature, and will experience a Coriolis force acting towards the east.

In all cases, the horizontal component of the Coriolis force on a particle of unit mass acts at right angles to the direction of motion, and the magnitude of $2\Omega \sin \theta$ times the magnitude of the local vector for the air velocity.

The vertical component of the Coriolis force also affects air particles moving along circles of latitude. For example, a particle moving eastward will experience an apparent decrease in weight as a result of the action of the vertical component of Coriolis force. Usually, this effect is exceedingly small compared to the gravitational attraction, and consequently it normally is disregarded.

Changes in Vorticity Relative to the Earth. There are many circumstances when portions of the atmosphere move horizontally over large distances of 100 km or more. For practical calculations of the motion of these large bodies of air, only the component of the earth's rotation around an axis normal to the horizon needs to be considered. The spinning motion of the earth then contributes to the vertical component of vorticity. The total, or absolute vorticity a in the vertical direction is defined as the sum of the relative component b and the planetary component, the Coriolis parameter f. Angular momentum tends to be conserved in an element of frictionless gas. Under this condition, the change in the absolute component then is found to be proportional to the product of the absolute vorticity times the horizontal change in velocity. This means that absolute vorticity increases with horizontal convergence and decreases with horizontal divergence, provided that angular momentum tends to be conserved. If the air remains at approximately constant density, the inflow of horizontal motion in convergence is coupled with vertical stretching, and horizontal divergence requires vertical shrinking. The famous Swedish-American geophysicist C. G. Rossby applied these princi-

ples to the changes in absolute vorticity, and found that in many
cases the ratio of the absolute vorticity to the height of the air
column containing the vorticity tended to be constant. That is,

$$\frac{a}{d} = \frac{b+f}{d} \approx \text{const.} \qquad (4.21)$$

for a column of frictionless air of height d. This expression is one
of the more useful relations that can be applied to large-scale
motion in the atmosphere. Equation (4.21) implies that large
bodies of air moving incompressibly across latitude circles as indicated in Fig. 4-13 should exhibit changes in vorticity in a particular way. Noting that vorticity is positive in the sense of the earth's
rotation, a column of air of height d moving poleward may either
slow up in rotation relative to earth, or may increase its height
since f increases [Fig. 4-13(A)]. If on the other hand the column

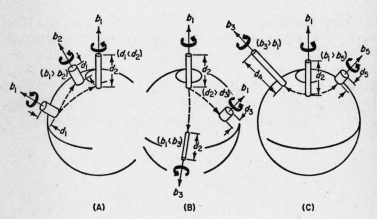

FIG. 4-13   Stretching of a column of spinning air as it moves over the earth.

turns equatorward as drawn in Fig. 4-13(B), f decreases so that increases in the column's spin relative to earth or a decrease in its
height, or both, may occur. When the column tends to move along
circles of latitude, f remains constant so that the stretching or
shrinking of the column during convergence or divergence must
either increase or decrease b, as shown in Fig. 4-13(C).

NEWTON'S SECOND LAW AND
SOME SIMPLE WINDS

For the earthbound observer, Newton's Second Law as applied to the atmosphere may be written in a manner that incorporates all of the forces acting on the air. The acceleration of an element of air must be equal to the vector sum of the forces per unit mass acting on that particle of fluid. If the vertical component of the Coriolis force is neglected,

$$\mathbf{a} = \frac{d\mathbf{q}}{dt} = -\frac{1}{\rho} \operatorname{grad} p + \frac{\mathbf{T}}{\rho} - \mathbf{g} + \mathbf{C_h}. \qquad (4.22)$$

$$\underset{\substack{\text{Acceleration} \\ \text{relative to} \\ \text{the earth}}}{} = \underset{\substack{\text{Pressure-} \\ \text{gradient} \\ \text{force per} \\ \text{unit mass}}}{} + \underset{\substack{\text{frictional} \\ \text{force per} \\ \text{unit mass}}}{} + \text{gravity} + \underset{\substack{\text{Coriolis} \\ \text{force per} \\ \text{unit mass}}}{}$$

Equation (4.22) serves as a general framework for describing atmospheric motion. If this differential equation could be solved for various initial conditions and boundary conditions, the atmospheric dynamicists' theoretical troubles would be over. Since Eq. (4.22), taken in all three dimensions, is exceedingly complicated, there are no complete mathematical solutions to this relation. Therefore in practice, meteorologists try to find simplified mathematical models for predicting atmospheric motion. This often is accomplished by examining each force in Eq. (4.22) for its importance in governing certain kinds of wind patterns under particular atmospheric conditions. If certain terms are believed to be unimportant for a given wind system, these terms may be disregarded in constructing a theoretical model. As in all of theoretical physics, the success of such models depends on how well they describe and predict the natural phenomenon in question.

In classical meteorology, there are several simple classes of "equilibrium" winds that would exist if the atmosphere behaved ideally. Perhaps the simplest classes of motion are those in which there is no acceleration relative to the earth. One example of this kind of equilibrium already has been touched upon in Chapter 3. When there is no vertical component of acceleration, and the vertical components of the frictional forces and the Coriolis force are negligible, Eq. (4.22) essentially reduces to the hydrostatic equation, Eq. (3.2).

The Geostrophic Wind. Another example of an air flow without acceleration which is very important to the meteorologist is the *geostrophic wind*. This kind of motion can arise when there is frictionless flow along straight streamlines running parallel to the earth's surface. If there is no horizontal acceleration in this case, the pressure-gradient force balances only the Coriolis force. Under these conditions, the Coriolis force opposes the pressure-gradient force, and the Coriolis force then must be directed normal to the lines of constant pressure (the isobars). The direction of the geostrophic wind, as determined by the direction of the horizontal pressure gradient, lies parallel to isobars. That is, the streamlines for geostrophic flow coincide with the isobars. For the Northern Hemisphere, the relation between the geostrophic wind v_G, the pressure-gradient force, and the Coriolis force is shown in Fig. 4-14. The magnitude of the geostrophic wind depends on the lati-

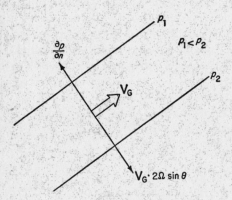

FIG. 4-14 Geostrophic motion.

tude angle θ, the size of the pressure gradient, and the air density. The greater the geostrophic wind, the steeper the pressure gradient, the lower the latitude, and the lower the density (the higher the altitude).

Effect of Friction on the Geostrophic Wind. Although the winds are qualitatively geostrophic at altitudes above 500 to 1000 meters, the influence of friction causes the winds to slow down and to veer across isobars at lower heights in the atmosphere. Qualitatively, friction reduces the wind speed in layers of air near the ground, causing a reduction in the Coriolis force. At the surface, the Coriolis force alone becomes too small to balance the pressure-gradient force so that the latter in combination with friction tends to dominate the flow, and air will flow with a component across isobars towards lower pressures.

Since friction essentially affects both the speed and direction of the wind, vectors representing the winds will begin near the surface with low speed in a cross-isobar direction, will increase in magnitude, and will shift in direction towards the isobars as the retarding effect of friction decreases with altitude. Hence a pilot balloon released at the ground in the Northern Hemisphere would ascend in such a way that it would curve ideally towards the right as its altitude increases.

Accelerated Air Flow. In the earth's atmosphere, the geostrophic wind constitutes an equilibrium configuration for the horizontal motion in the same sense that the hydrostatic balance determines an equilibrium structure for the vertical flow. The difference between the actual wind pattern and the geostrophic model is called the *ageostrophic wind*, $\mathbf{v}_A$. Meteorologists often analyze the motion of the earth's atmosphere in terms of the ageostrophic component.

The relation between the acceleration of air without friction to the ageostrophic wind can be determined easily from Eq. (4.22). The velocity of the air is defined as:

$$\mathbf{q} = \mathbf{v}_G + \mathbf{v}_A.$$

Then the horizontal acceleration reads:

$$\left(\frac{d\mathbf{q}}{dt}\right)_{\mathrm{h}} = \left(-\frac{1}{\rho}\operatorname{grad} p\right)_{\mathrm{h}} + f(\mathbf{v}_G + \mathbf{v}_A). \qquad (4.23)$$

However, the geostrophic component of the wind field is given by:

$$0 = \left(-\frac{1}{\rho}\operatorname{grad} p\right)_{\mathrm{h}} + f\mathbf{v}_G. \qquad (4.24)$$

Subtracting Eq. (4.24) from Eq. (4.23), we find that

$$\left(\frac{d\mathbf{q}}{dt}\right)_{\mathrm{h}} = f\mathbf{v}_A. \qquad (4.25)$$

Thus, the horizontal ageostrophic component of the frictionless wind is proportional to the acceleration of the air, and is directed at right angles to it to the left.

Frequently, the air flows steadily in a curved path around zones of high or low pressure. Whenever this situation exists, the centripetal acceleration must be taken into account in the balance of forces. We have already seen how a cyclostrophic wind develops when the centripetal force equals only the pressure-gradient force. The centripetal acceleration also can be balanced only by the Coriolis force per unit mass. This defines *inertial motion*. For a given latitude, particles of air undergoing this kind of flow will rotate in circular paths whose radius equals the ratio of the fluid velocity q and the Coriolis parameter f. If the latitude changes during inertial motion, the circular paths are changed to elongated loops. The turning in inertial motion will be clockwise in the Northern Hemisphere, and counterclockwise in the Southern Hemisphere.

If the centripetal acceleration is balanced both by the Coriolis force and the pressure-gradient force, a *gradient wind* develops. If the air moves around a region of high pressure (anticyclonic flow), the centripetal acceleration q^2/r is positive, and the centripetal acceleration consequently has the same direction as the Coriolis force per unit mass as indicated in Fig. 4-15(A). If, however, the wind blows around a region of low pressure (cyclonic flow), the centripetal acceleration is negative and is directed opposite to the Coriolis effect as drawn in Fig. 4-15(B).

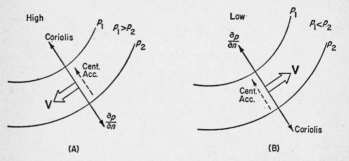

FIG. 4-15 The gradient wind for cyclonic and anticyclonic flow in the Northern Hemisphere.

The Link Between the Vertical Structure of the Atmosphere and the Winds. So far we have looked at the behavior of horizontal air motion as predicted by simplifications of Newton's Second Law written in terms of air density. This form is inconvenient for many calculations because the density of air varies with altitude. Furthermore, the motion of air is also closely connected with the position of isobars, which are not easily traced to level surfaces. In meteorological practice, these difficulties are alleviated somewhat by referring the horizontal air motion to surfaces of constant pressure, which can be calculated easily from temperature and pressure data taken, for example, by radiosonde balloons.

Typical records showing the height of constant-pressure surfaces are indicated on weather maps such as the one in Fig. 4-16. If we were to take a vertical section of this map through the line at 60°N, it would look like the diagram in Fig. 4-17. Here the section through the contours of the 500 mb surface show domes and depressions which are analogous to the hills and valleys displayed on topographical maps of the earth's surface.

The horizontal pressure gradient can be found simply from changes in height of the constant-pressure contours for different locations. To illustrate this, a cut is made along the x coordinate across the contours on surfaces of constant pressure as indicated in Fig. 4.18. Using the hydrostatic equation for the vertical pressure gradient, and dividing by the increment dx between horizontal points, we find that

$$\frac{1}{\rho}\left(\frac{dp}{dx}\right) = g\left(\frac{dz}{dx}\right). \qquad (4.26)$$

Generalizing this relation, we can say that the vector corresponding to the geostrophic wind can be written as:

$$\mathbf{v}_G = \frac{g}{f}(\text{grad } z)_h, \qquad (4.27)$$

where the direction of the vector corresponding to the pressure gradient is taken perpendicular to the contours along the surfaces of constant pressure. The geostrophic wind then has a direction along the contours with the lower values of z to the left in the Northern Hemisphere.

FIG. 4-16 Contours of the 500 mb pressure surface, Northern Hemisphere, 1200 GCT, Feb. 1, 1959. The curves represent altitude times ten in meters. (From U. S. Weather Bureau, *Synoptic Weather Maps*, February 1959.)

The Thermal Wind. Because warm air has a lower density than cold air, the vertical distance between any two surfaces of constant pressure must be greater in warm regions than in cold regions. Thus, when the atmosphere is warm, the pressure changes more slowly with height than under cold conditions.

Masses of cool air often lie next to masses of warm air in the atmosphere. Under these conditions, the vertical concentration of isobars must be greater in the cold regions than in the warm

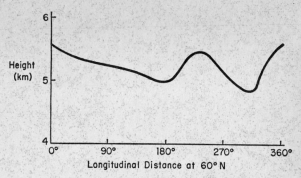

FIG. 4-17 A vertical cut through the pressure surface in Fig. 4-16, taken at latitude 60°N.

zones, and an increasingly steep gradient in pressure can develop as indicated in Fig. 4-19. The downward slope of isobaric surfaces to the left as shown here will result in a geostrophic wind directed into the page. In the Northern Hemisphere, there is normally cool air over the pole to the north, and warmer air near the equator to the south. From the corresponding structure in Fig. 4-19, the persistence of a westerly wind at upper tropospheric levels should occur as is observed. In the lower stratosphere, however, the temperature gradients are reversed as indicated in Fig. 3-1. Thus, the prevailing westerlies in the northern mid-latitudes increase to a

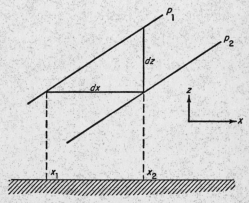

FIG. 4-18 An idealized vertical cross section through contours of constant pressure.

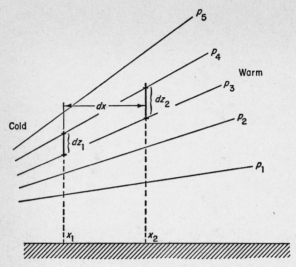

FIG. 4-19 Sloping surfaces of constant pressure and regions of different air density.

maximum intensity in the upper troposphere, and then decrease upward in the lower stratosphere.

The change in the geostrophic wind per unit change in altitude is called the *thermal wind*. Using Eq. (4.26), we can estimate its magnitude. The difference between the component of the geostrophic wind in the x direction, say at two altitudes (1) and (2), is:

$$v_{G2} - v_{G1} = \frac{g}{f}\left(\frac{dz_2}{dx} - \frac{dz_1}{dx}\right) = \frac{g}{f}\frac{d\Delta}{dx},$$

where dz_2 and dz_1 denote the change in height or the thickness between the same two isobars at two different horizontal locations along the x direction. The term Δ represents the difference between the two thicknesses dz_2 and dz_1 for the change dx. This relation can be generalized in vector form as:

$$\mathbf{v}_T = \mathbf{v}_{G2} - \mathbf{v}_{G1} = \frac{g}{f}(\text{grad }\Delta)_h. \qquad (4.28)$$

The direction of the thermal wind thus depends on the vector difference between $\mathbf{v}_{G2}$ and $\mathbf{v}_{G1}$, and is directed along the thickness lines given by Δ with high values to the right.

Summary of Equilibrium Winds. We can list in Table 4-1 the principal kinds of balanced horizontal flow which may develop in

TABLE 4–1. *Summary of Important Equilibrium Winds*

Wind	*Balance*
Geostrophic Wind	Coriolis force = pressure-gradient force
Gradient Wind	Centripetal force = pressure-gradient force + Coriolis force
Inertial Wind	Centripetal force = Coriolis force
Cyclostrophic Wind	Centripetal force = pressure-gradient force

an idealized frictionless atmosphere. Within these systems of winds, all of the combinations of the three forces involved in frictionless motion appear. However, the first two ideal winds listed in Table 4-1 are of primary importance in atmospheric motion. Both the concepts of the geostrophic wind and the gradient wind will arise in Chapters 5 and 7 in explaining the properties of the large-scale air motion. True inertial motion is extremely rare in the atmosphere because of the presence of pressure gradients and the influences of friction. As we shall see in Chapter 7, cyclostrophic motion only becomes of interest in hurricane and typhoon development near the equator where the deviating effect of the Coriolis force is small.

Frictional effects are observed near the earth's surface or in regions where there is strong wind shear. Therefore, at altitudes above about 1 km, there is a strong tendency for the atmosphere to approach geostrophic flow as long as the wind is blowing in a straight path. For curvilinear flow at high altitude, the gradient wind represents the horizontal motion at equilibrium.

The shear in the geostrophic wind field, the thermal wind, can be estimated by examining changes in the mass of air packed in between surfaces of constant pressure.

5 Patterns of Larger Scale Atmospheric Motion

THE GENERAL CIRCULATION

The motion of the atmosphere at any instant consists of a net reaction of the body of air to forces acting on a wide variety of scales. If the winds are averaged over very long periods of time, the faster-varying, smaller-scale phenomena become largely suppressed, and only the more slowly changing and larger modes of flow are revealed. The average structure of largest patterns of motion of the atmosphere makes up the subject of *the general circulation*. Because of their mutual interaction, it really is not possible to split the global patterns of circulation away from the smaller-scale phenomena. However, it is possible to learn a great deal about certain features of the winds without considering flow on scales smaller than about 1000 km. Once the averaged circulation is understood, it can serve as a useful framework for interpreting most features of the larger scale movement in the atmosphere.

Observed Average Circulation. In recent years, the picture of global circulation in the troposphere has become relatively complete, particularly in the Northern Hemisphere. Although the detailed structure of the average flow still eludes quantitative analysis, considerable progress has been made towards a fundamental understanding of certain important features of the average motion on the larger scales. To get a picture of the atmosphere's general circulation, let us briefly outline some important features of the known observations.

When the wind patterns are averaged around zonal rings (longitudinally) over long periods of time, the circulation becomes characterized by three zonal belts of surface winds in each hemisphere, similar to that drawn in Fig. 5-3(B). In all seasons, there exist, on the average, belts of easterlies near the poles, above 60° latitude, and in latitudes below 30° latitude. These westward-flowing currents are separated by a zone of westerlies in the mid-latitudes. The westerlies in the middle latitudes extend to all altitudes while the intermittent polar easterlies are very shallow. The belts of rather steady, easterly trade winds in the tropics are much deeper, extending at times well into the stratosphere. Moreover, the strong westerly winds at upper levels tend to tilt the latitudinal belt equatorward from about 30° latitude at the surface to roughly 15° at the topopause. Seasonal fluctuations cause the belts of easterlies to oscillate 15° latitude or more about the equator.

The region near the equator, below 10° latitude, consists of a zone of convergence of air near the surface. This region exhibits intermittent weak winds that have given it the name of the *doldrums*. The convergence zone tends to migrate seasonally as far as 15° north and south of the equator in places. Seasonally, signs of bands of shallow westerlies also may be observed at times near the equator. These winds are superimposed on the trade winds, and appear to have a direct connection with monsoonal storms.

The tropical atmosphere exhibits much more of a barotropic structure than the mid-latitude zones. Therefore, the thermal wind components (p. 80) are relatively small in this region. Near the equator, the Coriolis force is negligible so that air tends to flow across isobars rather than, geostrophically, along isobars.

The subtropical easterlies, and the mid-latitude westerlies are separated at the surface by a calm zone of high pressure located at the surface roughly at 30° latitude. This region is called the *horse latitudes*, which are believed to be named for the numerous bodies of horses floating at sea in these regions during the seventeenth century. Sailing ships traveling to the New World at this time often were becalmed for long periods in this zone of high pressure. With limited supplies of food and water, there was no choice but to reduce their "consuming" cargo of animals in mid-ocean.

Perhaps the most striking feature of the mid-latitude winds is the jet stream. This region of high-speed flow with velocities up to 200 mph is located near the tropopause, at altitudes corresponding to about 200 mb pressure. The region where the westerlies are concentrated constitutes a strongly baroclinic part of the atmosphere. Thus, the zonal path of maximum speed in the westerlies is directly associated with the atmosphere's baroclinic structure in the mid-latitudes (See also pp. 78-80). In the Northern Hemisphere, the westerlies in the mid-latitudes are stronger in the winter than in summer, when the jet stream also is closer to the equator. Though observational data are more scanty in the Southern Hemisphere, the seasonal variations appear to be qualitatively similar to those of the Northern Hemisphere.

When the longitudinal variations in flow remain in the picture, persistent local effects appear. Typical averaged streamlines at the earth's surface shown in Figs. 5-1(A) and 5-1(B) for months of January and July display marked zonal irregularities. Because of the variety of differences in heating, and the variations in surface friction between land and sea, the streamline patterns resemble only superficially the ideal of three uniformly distributed zonal belts of winds shown in Fig. 5-3(B). In both seasons the maps in Fig. 5-1 show large diverging swirls over the oceans, which are called *warm subtropical highs,* and pronounced regions of equatorial convergence. In both hemispheres, the patterns of average flow reveal that the westerlies undulate meridionally in irregular stationary waves instead of exhibiting purely zonal flow. Because of the effects of differences in distribution of land masses there is evidently a stronger tendency for zonal motion in the Southern Hemisphere than in the Northern Hemisphere. Although the surface streamlines do not indicate it, the strongest perturbation in the Southern Hemisphere flow at higher altitude appears to be the South American continent. Australia, Africa, and India seem to have somewhat less influence on the upper-level winds. In the Northern Hemisphere during winter, a strong divergent

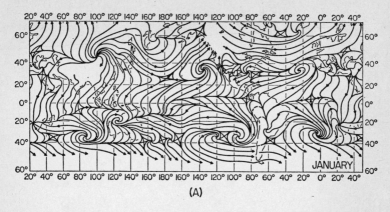

(A)

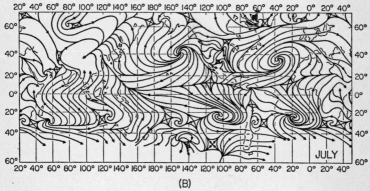

(B)

FIG. 5-1 Average streamlines of air flow at the earth's surface in January (A) and July (B). [From Y. Mintz and G. Dean, "The observed field of motion of the atmosphere," Geophys. Res. Papers, No. 17, Air Force Cambridge Research Laboratories, Bedford, Massachusetts, 1952. See also S. L. Hess, *Introduction to Theoretical Meteorology* (Holt, Rinehart and Winston Co., New York, 1959), p. 328.]

vortex develops over Siberia (region of cold high pressure), but relatively persistent convergent eddies form over the Pacific and Atlantic oceans near 60°N. These two more or less permanent zones of low pressure are called the *Aleutian* and the *Icelandic Lows*. These regions of cyclonic circulation become much weaker in the summer months, but nevertheless they remain in the picture of the average wind field. The response of the atmosphere to relatively low continental temperatures in winter, contrasted to

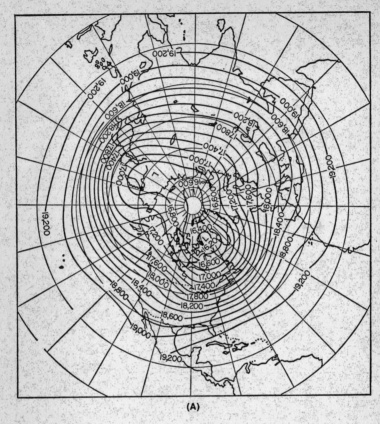

(A)

relatively high temperatures in summer, is reflected in the monsoonal change in circulation over Asia. In this region, a convergent regime of relatively low pressure in summer takes the place of the divergent zone of the cold high in winter.

Assuming that the flow at high altitude is geostrophic (p. 74), on the average, the patterns of upper-level winds can be traced by the direction of the isobars. The mean surfaces for 500 mb pressure, called *normal charts,* as found for January and July are drawn in Figs. 5-2(A) and 5-2(B). These charts are particularly useful to the meteorologist because they give information about winds roughly in the position of the center of the vertical distribution of atmospheric mass. The maps indicate that the zonal flow in the Northern Hemisphere, for example, at altitudes of about 5

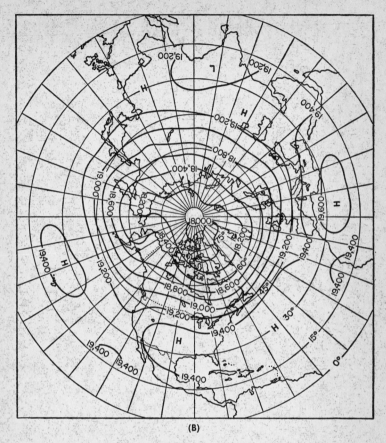

(B)

FIG. 5-2 Normal 500 mb charts, Northern Hemisphere: (A) January, (B) July. Altitude of contours in feet. [From H. R. Byers, *General Meteorology* (McGraw-Hill Book Co., New York, 1959), 3rd Ed., pp. 267-268. Used by permission.]

km is asymmetric about the polar region of low pressure. The bulges in the zonal circulation reflect the positions at upper levels of the Aleutian and Icelandic Lows. In addition, the band of high pressure in the latitudes around 30° tends to break up into a cellular structure over the oceans in the summer seasons. The summer partitioning into cells does not appear to be so pronounced in the Southern Hemisphere, but the general structure of circulation seems to be qualitatively similar in both hemispheres.

Despite the similarities in overall behavior of the atmosphere over the two hemispheres, some important differences in detailed wind structure have been observed. For example, there is evidence that the westerlies in the mid-latitudes appear to be stronger in summer than in winter over the Southern Hemisphere. However, the reverse is true of the Northern Hemisphere. This curious difference seems to be closely related to thermal effects stemming from the fact that surface of the earth in the Southern Hemisphere is covered mainly by water, while the earth's surface in the Northern Hemisphere is largely land.

A Simple Model of Atmospheric Circulation. Even though meteorology has not reached a stage where the detailed structure of the general circulation patterns are fully predictable, many features can be explained by relatively simple theory. We already have mentioned that by 1735, Sir George Hadley published the primitive beginnings of a theory for planetary circulation using ideas based on hydrostatic stability. Hadley's idea pictured the meridional flow as a single cell with rising warm air at the equator, and sinking cool air at the pole, as sketched in Fig. 5-3(A).

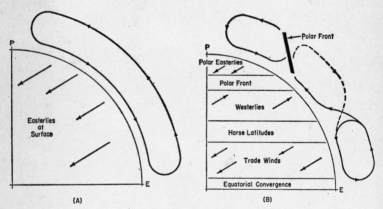

FIG. 5-3 Idealized meridional circulation in the atmosphere, and the belts of prevailing winds: (A) Hadley cell, (B) three-cell model.

Without east-west gradients in pressure, the one-celled circulation would be the same at all longitudinal circles, and in the absence of friction, absolute angular momentum M would be conserved in the plane of zonal rings. Using the notation in Fig. 4-6,

$$M = \text{const.} = \Omega R^2 \cos^2 \theta + uR \cos \theta, \qquad (5.1)$$

where the first term on the right refers to angular momentum of a ring fixed to the earth, and the second term denotes the angular momentum of air moving relative to the fixed ring. From (5.1),

$$u = \frac{\text{const}}{R \cos \theta} - \Omega R \cos \theta.$$

Thus by conserving angular momentum, the wind speed u relative to the earth's surface would tend to increase as zonal rings of air move poleward, and would tend to decrease as zonal rings flow equatorward. Hence, in Hadley's cell, the poleward meridional flow at higher altitude should veer eastward, and the equatorward drift at the surface should shift westward.

In this scheme, the hypothetical easterlies near the surface at all latitudes would by friction remove angular momentum from the planet, and eventually would reduce its rate of rotation. This we know cannot be true because the earth's rotation is essentially constant. Furthermore, Hadley's model fails to account for the observed westerlies in the middle latitudes. Therefore, Hadley's theory is inadequate, and a more realistic model has to be conceived.

To explain the banded structure of zonal winds, a more modern picture of meridional circulation was devised during the period between 1930 and 1950 by the meteorologists T. Bergeron, C. G. Rossby, and others. Still maintaining the assumption of conservation of absolute angular momentum, these scientists proposed a three-celled model, sketched in Fig. 5-3(B). If a loss of heat by radiation from upper layers of warm air near the equator takes place at a rate corresponding to 1°-2°C per day, the air in the upper layers will tend to sink and spread out at the earth's surface somewhere near 30° latitude. As the cooled air settles to the ground it may continue to move poleward, or it may return toward the equator, thus completing the tropical cell. By conserving angular momentum, the equatorward component in the low latitudes would veer eastward, forming the observed belts of trade winds in the tropics. On the other hand, the poleward component of sinking air at the surface would give rise to westward flow which should increase in speed with latitude. Friction at the earth's surface would remove angular momentum from the pole-ward-moving air, producing a balanced state of moderate westerly winds in the middle latitudes. Near the poles, the net radiative loss of heat requires sinking as in the case of Hadley's model. The equatorward spread of this air near the ground should be accompanied by easterly winds, as observed. Developing zones of relatively sharp change in density, called *fronts,* are often observed when the cold easterly flow meets the warmer poleward-drifting air at the surface in the mid-latitudes.

Just taking into account the influences of radiative heat loss alone in Hadley's classical model has produced an explanation for the observed wind fields near the surface. However, this newer theory predicts incorrectly that the prevailing westerlies in the mid-latitudes should decrease with altitude, and eventually should develop an easterly component, provided that the angular momentum remains the same. The observed winds actually tend to increase with height up to the tropopause in the mid-latitude belt. In fact, meteorologists have found that the observed wind patterns rarely form complete zonal rings as indicated in Fig. 4-16. To avoid these difficulties the theoretical arguments again had to be modified and improved, by relaxing the requirement of conservation of angular momentum, and by incorporating the longitudinal pressure gradients into the model of the atmosphere.

Transport of Angular Momentum. In reality, of course, angular momentum in rings of air is not conserved because of the action of torques associated with east-west gradients in pressure, and with friction. In the middle latitudes, there are clearly permanent longitudinal asymmetries in atmospheric pressure (Fig. 5-2) which are partly associated with mountain barriers, and partly the result of local differences in heating of the atmosphere. The distributions in pressure over mountains tend to cause an extraction of angular momentum from the westerlies. Similarly, friction at the earth's surface removes angular momentum from the westerlies, but adds angular momentum to the easterlies. If the westerlies are not to die away in time, the loss in angular momentum has to be replaced by meridional transport.

The average transport of angular momentum in the meridional

A

B

PLATE I (A) A cumulonimbus cloud with small cumulus clouds near the ocean's surface. [Photo from National Institute of Oceanography, also from F. H. Ludlam and R. S. Scorer, *Cloud Study: A Pictorial Guide* (John Murray Publ., London, 1957).] (B) Looking down at a deck of cumulus clouds from above. (Photo by A. J. Aalders; see also WMO *International Cloud Atlas*, Vol. II, Plate 184.)

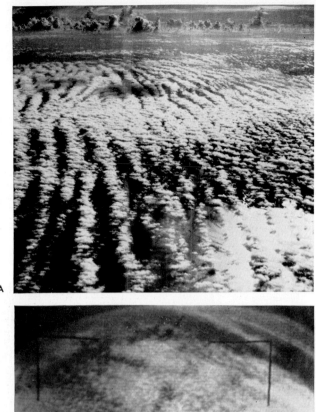

PLATE II   (A) Lines of cumulus clouds in the tropics. (Photo by V. G. Plank.) (B)
Cellular convection marked by clouds, taken from Tiros VIII satellite, July 18, 1964.
(ESSA Photo; Mon. Wea. Rev. **93**, p. 212.)

PLATE III Streaky cirrus clouds suggesting high winds aloft. (Photo by J. H. Con-
over; see also WMO *International Cloud Atlas*, Vol. II, Plate 133.)

PLATE IV   Clouds associated with the Sierra wave in the lee of the Sierra Nevada
Range in California. The lowest cloud, related to turbulence in the rotor, reaches
an altitude of about 6 km. The middle formation is a lenticular cloud located along
the crest of the lee wave at 10 km. The upper cloud is another lee wave cloud at 13
km altitude. (Photo by Betsy Woodward.)

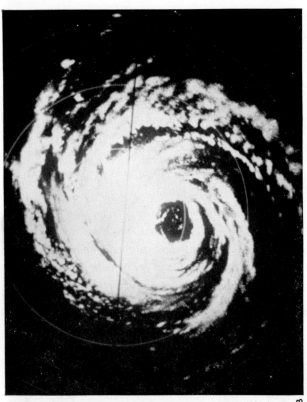

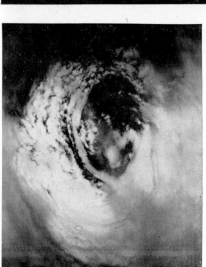

PLATE V Spinning motion in hurricanes. (A) The eye of Hurricane Betsy photographed from aircraft above 60,000 ft on Sept. 2, 1965. (Official U.S. Air Force Photograph.) (B) Hurricane Betsy as seen by radar Sept. 8, 1965. (ESSA Photo.) (C) Hurricane Betsy as observed from Tiros VIII satellite. The storm is located near 23°N, 75.5°W, Sept. 2, 1965. (ESSA Photo.)

PLATE VI   (A) A tornado vortex photographed on May 4, 1961 near Cheyenne, Okla.
(Photo by Bill Males.) (B) A waterspout near Deer Field Beach, Fla. (Photo by
M. Sait, courtesy of the U.S. Weather Bureau.)

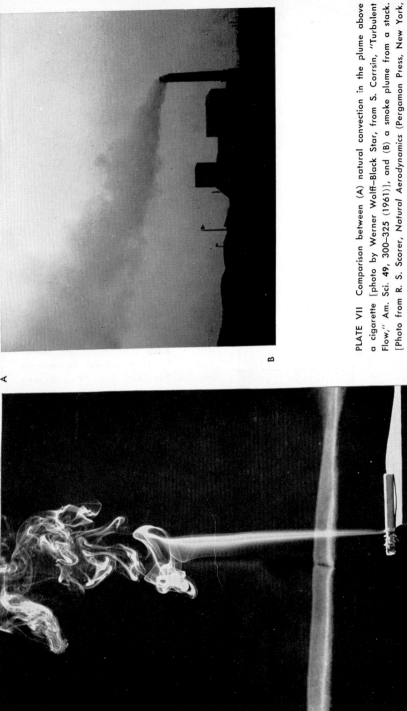

PLATE VII Comparison between (A) natural convection in the plume above a cigarette [photo by Werner Wolff—Black Star, from S. Corrsin, "Turbulent Flow," Am. Sci. **49**, 300–325 (1961)], and (B) a smoke plume from a stack. [Photo from R. S. Scorer, *Natural Aerodynamics* (Pergamon Press, New York, 1958), p. 208.]

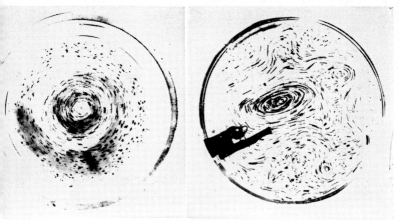

PLATE VIII Reversal streak photographs of convective circulation on the surface of fluid in a rotating pan: (A) axisymmetric regime, where $Ro \approx 2.6$, and (B) irregular wave regime, $Ro \approx 0.04$ [From D. Fultz, et al., "Studies of Thermal Convection in a Rotating Cylinder with some Implications for Large-Scale Atmospheric Motions," Meteorological Monographs 4, No. 21, pp. 22, 55 (1959), American Meteorological Society, Boston.]

PLATE IX A laboratory analogy to a thermal. [From R. S. Scorer, *Natural Aerodynamics* (Pergamon Press, New York, 1958), p. 164.]

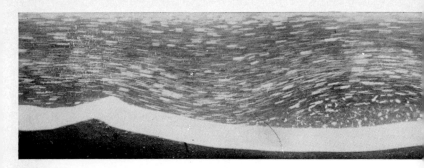

PLATE X A hydrodynamic model of flow over the Sierra Nevada mountain range showing the development of a single lee wave. The fluid is stratified with salt and water, where $Fr = 0.258$. [From R. R. Long, "A Laboratory Model of Air Flow over the Sierra Nevada Mountains," in *The Atmosphere and the Sea in Motion* (Rockefeller Inst. Press, New York, 1959), p. 377.]

A

B

PLATE XI (A) A laboratory model of a vortex involving buoyant convection. The rotation rate of the cylinder is 32 rpm, the fluid is water, and the vertical circulation is induced by bubbling air into the water at the axis of rotation. (B) A closer view of the dye streaks tracing vertical motion in the laboratory vortex.

plane is given by the factor M times the average meridional wind velocity $\langle v \rangle_{av}$:

$$M\langle v \rangle_{av} = R \cos \theta [\langle v \rangle_{av} \Omega R \cos \theta + \langle uv \rangle_{av}], \qquad (5.2)$$

where the angular brackets denote an average over long periods of time, given by the relation:

$$\langle v \rangle_{av} = \frac{1}{T} \int_0^T v(t) \, dt.$$

The role of fluctuations in the average motion becomes apparent if we define the instantaneous velocity of air in terms of the sum of an average value and a perturbation associated with the fluctuations in time of the winds:

$$\begin{array}{lll} \text{zonal,} & u = \langle u \rangle_{av} + u'; \\ \text{meridional,} & v = \langle v \rangle_{av} + v'. \end{array} \qquad (5.3)$$

Since the average of the perturbation velocities u' and v' is zero, the only part of Eq. (5.2) that contains these quantities is the term $\langle uv \rangle_{av}$, or

$$\langle uv \rangle_{av} = \langle u \rangle_{av} \langle v \rangle_{av} + \langle u'v' \rangle_{av}. \qquad (5.4)$$

Thus, the meridional transport in Eq. (5.2) contains (a) an Ω transport term, representing the meridional flux of angular momentum of the earth's rotation by the mean meridional flow, $\langle v \rangle_{av}$, (b) a drift term, denoting a transport of angular momentum from the mean zonal current by a non-geostrophic meridional drift, and (c) an eddy flux term, accounting for transport of zonal fluctuating momentum towards the polar cap by huge vortices or eddies, and by large planetary waves in the zonal winds. Both of these patterns are shown in Fig. 4-16.

Because there can be no net gain or loss of air in zonal rings over long periods of time, the average meridional velocity $\langle v \rangle_{av}$ in a ring whose depth corresponds to that of the atmosphere must be zero. Hence, the total Ω transport also must be zero for a zonal ring of air of atmospheric depth. Indeed, the studies of wind observations in the tropics have indicated that a poleward transport of angular momentum by the Ω term at high altitude is just balanced by an equatorward flow associated with the steady trade winds at the surface.

If the geostrophic wind is integrated around a zonal ring, the integral must be zero since there can be only a single value of the pressure at a given point on the ring. Therefore, the drift term can only contribute to meridional transport of angular momentum through the ageostrophic component of the wind, $\mathbf{v}_A$ (p. 75), which in turn comes from the contribution of the disturbances. There can be a positive drift of momentum poleward only if the mean zonal component of the wind $\langle u \rangle_{av}$ is positively directed (west winds). Thus, poleward drift will be most effective above 15° latitude near the tropopause where $\langle u \rangle_{av}$ is strongest from the west, with relative equatorward drift in weaker winds at higher and lower altitude.

There is strong evidence that ageostrophic flow is responsible for transport of angular momentum in the tropics, but that the eddy term controls heat and momentum transport in the middle and high latitudes. The eddy flux can only contribute to poleward meridional flow of angular momentum if $\langle u'v' \rangle_{av}$ is positive. This implies that circumstances must exist frequently for conditions in which a strong zonal flow accompanies a strong poleward flow. Patterns of motion such as those in Fig. 4-16 often show such conditions along the wave-like disturbances in the mid-latitudes. For example, the pattern of isobars drawn in Fig. 5-4 is typical of upper-level winds in the Northern Hemisphere. Under these circumstances, strong gradients in pressure appear east of troughs in the waves, while weaker gradients develop west of the troughs.

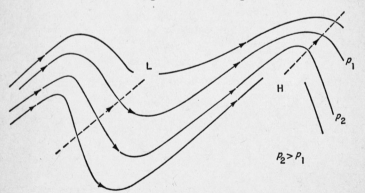

FIG. 5-4 A typical wave configuration in the westerlies.

This means that large positive values of u are found in cases where v is positive, and consequently $\langle u'v' \rangle_{av}$ around a zonal ring can be positive.

Examination of the available information about the winds suggests that the poleward drift of angular momentum, primarily through the eddy flux to the westerlies in the mid-latitudes, with subsequent downward transport, is roughly sufficient to balance the removal of angular momentum extracted by friction at the surface of the earth in this region.

Thus, based on present evidence, the achievement of a balance in angular momentum in the atmosphere appears to take place by direct ageostrophic, meridional flow in the low latitudes, combined with an eddy flux associated with the ever-present vortices and waves in the large-scale motion of air over the mid-latitudes.

Energy Conversion and the General Circulation. In Chapter 1, we introduced the idea that the atmosphere is a gigantic heat engine. The fuel supplied by the sun's radiant energy enters the atmosphere primarily in low latitudes and is pumped poleward to balance the deficit in energy in high latitudes resulting from losses by radiation. In the past 20 years, careful study of meteorological observations contained in synoptic charts like Fig. 4-16 has made it possible to arrive at relatively good estimates of the poleward flow of heat. The results of these investigations have indicated that the huge swirls and wave-like fluctuations that transport angular momentum poleward above latitudes of about 30° also must account for the bulk of heat transport. However, the large eddies fall short of the required transport of heat in the belts of trade winds, thus confirming our picture that direct transport associated with a meridional component of motion gives rise to poleward flow of heat in the tropical atmosphere.

Using high-speed computers, meteorologists such as Prof. Norman Phillips at the Massachusetts Institute of Technology recently have discovered that solar energy is converted to kinetic energy of the average circulation primarily through the action of the disturbances in the patterns of the general circulation. Hence, the atmosphere's heating is converted into average potential energy during the rising of masses of warm air. Then, instead of taking a path prescribed by classical theories, which predict a transfer from the average potential energy directly to the average of zonal flow, the atmosphere evidently uses the indirect route of transfer via the potential energy of disturbances. Therefore, it is the disturbances that hold the key to understanding the behavior of the atmosphere. These daily and hourly fluctuations on a planetary scale are closely tied to the smaller-scale phenomena including those ranging from the huge eddies, down through the towering convection of cumulus clouds on to the tiny rolling gusts of wind causing phenomena like the "cat's paw" ripples on lakes.

Meteorologists have solved many of the mysteries of the gross picture of the general circulation. However, like Plato in his *Republic*, atmospheric scientists have just begun to see the faintest rays of the light of "truth" about the vast, infinitely detailed, interlocking structure of atmospheric motion. Before the atmosphere can be considered quantitatively understood in the sense of predictability, much more effort must go into new theoretical studies, as well as much more extensive and systematic observations of the winds.

FLUCTUATIONS IN THE LARGE-SCALE MOTION

The equations of motion, Eq. (4.22), provide an extremely rich source from which the wide variety of atmospheric phenomena may be deduced. To attempt to reconstruct from Eq. (4.22) the known features of the fluctuating atmosphere, and how the perturbations fit together to produce the observed winds, is beyond the scope of this book. Nevertheless, we can briefly cover a few interesting features of atmospheric motion on several scales to focus attention on the complexities of the variety of flow patterns. Let us begin by considering the largest-scale perturbations in more detail. Later, in the succeeding chapters we shall focus attention on different kinds of smaller-scale phenomena.

As indicated in Fig. 4-16, the striking feature of the "short time" fluctuations in the large-scale flow consist of wave-like perturbations, which sometimes fold over into closed asymmetric vortices around regions of low or high pressure. In between the wave-cellular structure in the mid-latitudes at higher altitudes flows the strong current, the jet stream.

Rossby Waves. The waves and swirls in the westerlies can develop through the dynamics of either barotropic fluids, or baroclinic fluids. The longest atmospheric waves, planetary waves, are named for C. G. Rossby, who first discussed in 1939 their origins in a barotropic flow.

Rossby applied a form of Eq. (4.21), called *the vorticity theorem,*

$$\frac{d}{dt}\left[\frac{(f+b)}{d}\right] = 0, \tag{5.5}$$

to a broad westerly current that undulates like a wave to the northward and southward in a volume of air of constant height d. He found that for barotropic conditions the oscillation of a sinusoidal wave in the current which satisfies the condition of Eq. (5.5) depends strongly on the change in the Coriolis parameter with change in meridional distance, β:

$$\beta \equiv \frac{\partial f}{\partial y} = \frac{2\Omega \cos \theta}{R}. \tag{5.6}$$

The difference between the velocity of the basic current U and the phase speed c of the wave is given by:

$$U - c = \frac{\beta \lambda^2}{4\pi^2}, \tag{5.7}$$

where λ is the wave length. When c is positive, waves move west to east, and $U - c$ gives relatively small wave lengths. If c is negative, waves regress to the westward, but the velocity difference $U - c$ is large, yielding larger wave lengths. In many cases in the atmosphere, $U - c$ ranges from 10-50 meters $\sec^{-1}$, giving the number of planetary waves around the earth from 3 to 6, with wave lengths of several thousand kilometers.

To develop wave-like motion in the westerly flow of air, some kind of disturbance must initially set off the north-south undulation. One type of perturbation comes from mountain barriers. The effect of such obstacles illustrates another application of Eq. (5.2). Suppose we have a ridge oriented north-south over which flows a straight, uniform westerly current having no relative vorticity. We disregard friction by assuming that changes in vorticity are related only to curvature of the flow. Furthermore, it is assumed that a "rigid" lid, say the tropopause, exists on the atmosphere, or the perturbation extends only to a finite height, as indicated in Fig. 5-5(A). As the air flows up over the mountains, the

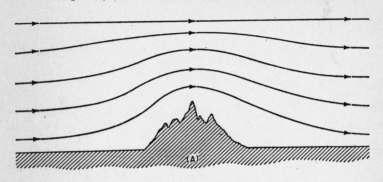

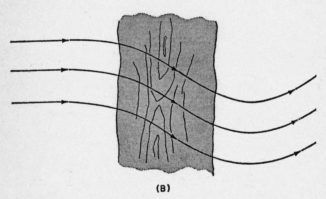

FIG. 5-5 An inertial oscillation developing in the lee of a mountain range.

height of an individual element of air tends to decrease, causing by the arguments in Fig. 4-13 an anticyclonic curvature in the horizontal streamlines [Fig. 5-5(B)]. At the top of the barrier, the minimum height of the air parcel is reached, and to the leeward side, the depth begins to increase again to its original value. The increase in d results in a return to zero relative vorticity, leaving the descending flow directed towards southeast. However, as the air sweeps past the ridge to a lower latitude, it begins to take on cyclonic curvature. To the leeward of the barrier the depth remains constant again, and the current becomes controlled by the variation in f with latitude alone. Thus, the wind pattern will tend to oscillate back and forth as a result of the β-effect.

This crude model dealing with the effect of mountain barriers can be used [1] to explain observed troughs of low pressure that often develop in zonal winds to the lee of mountain ranges. Hence, the sequences of nearly stationary ridges and troughs in the winds at upper levels in the mid-latitudes may be related to atmospheric disturbances caused by the presence of mountain ranges (orographic perturbations).

The long waves associated with the β-effect are not the only possible modes of wave-like disturbances on a planetary scale. It is known from observations and the theoretical work of scientists such as J. Charney, E. T. Eady, and E. Lorenz that other planetary waves may develop as a result of baroclinic instability. A very interesting analogy to baroclinic waves in the atmosphere was discovered and studied in a laboratory experiment a few years ago in the 1950s by D. Fultz and co-workers at the University of Chicago, and by R. Hide, now at the Massachusetts Institute of Technology.

Laboratory models of atmospheric circulation originated nearly a century ago with the Berlin physician-meteorologist, Friedrich Vettin. He observed a thermal circulation analogous to a Hadley cell [Fig. 5-3(A)] in a large rotating tank of air heated at the rim (the equator), and cooled with ice at the center (the pole). Vettin did not realize the importance of the rotation rate in his experiments, and consequently, he apparently was not able to duplicate the wave phenomena associated with the mid-latitude westerlies. Fultz and his colleagues, however, followed a clue of Rossby's, and discovered that the parameter, $U/\Omega L$, (L = length scale, and U = a characteristic wind velocity) was of central importance in finding hydrodynamic analogies to planetary wave phenomena. Using flat-bottomed rotating pans or rotating annuli

[1] See, for example, S. L. Hess, *Introduction to Theoretical Meteorology* (Henry Holt and Co., New York), 1959, 362 pages.

filled with water, heated at the rim and cooled at the center, these scientists made the following observations: At high Rossby number, Ro $(= U/\Omega L)$, or low rotation rates, the familiar axially symmetric Hadley circulation appeared as shown by the streaks in Plate VIII(A). Moving into a regime of moderately large Ro, the increase in rotation rate causes a breakdown in the meridional flow which is replaced by steady patterns of Rossby waves in the westerly jet streams appearing on the water surface midway between the rim and the axis of rotation. For still smaller Ro, and even higher rotation rates, the surface flow breaks down into irregular waves accompanied by discontinuous jets as suggested in Plate VIII(B). Inside the fluid, closed circulations and discontinuities in density developed in this case that appeared to be quite analogous to atmospheric motion on a large scale.

Since no analogy for the β-effect exists for flow of stratified fluids over a rotating flat surface, the waves in the dishpan experiments must have baroclinic origins. Nevertheless, the waves look remarkably like the inertial oscillations, the Rossby waves, induced by the influence of the earth's curvature.

The experiments of Fultz, Hide, and others are of considerable interest to meteorologists. They have contributed to a better understanding of thermal circulations as influenced by rotation, and the sharp changes with Ro provided further qualitative evidence that two different idealized mechanisms could take place in the atmosphere's thermally driven meridional circulation. The regime of high Ro, giving the axisymmetric flow of a Hadley-like cell is analogous to air motion in tropical regions, while the irregular regime of smaller Ro is very suggestive of the behavior of the mid-latitude belt of westerlies.

Frontal Discontinuities and the Jet Stream. The appearance of sharp contrasts in density over distances of 10-50 km between large masses of air in the mid-latitudes is nearly as common a feature as clouds in the troposphere.[2] The regions of strong change in fluid properties appear as discontinuities on weather maps covering

---

[2] The passage of fronts over the earth's surface often can be felt by sharp changes in temperature and violent storm activity. Many a case of pneumonia has developed when people go out in winter and spring unprepared for an onrushing front.

thousands of kilometers. It is remarkable that such sharp gradients also occur in the thermal circulations of water in a rotating pan. Though it has not been proven conclusively on theoretical grounds, one might easily deduce from these observations that the formation of fronts is a natural consequence of convective heat transport in a rotating fluid.

Although it is not possible for masses of fluid of different density to lie side by side at rest because of vertical differences in pressure, fluid movement accompanied by rotation certainly can give rise to stabilization of a vertical interface between two fluids. We can demonstrate this effect by considering a simple example of two bodies of gas, of density ρ_1 and ρ_2, having steady velocities of u_1 and u_2, and passing next to each other as drawn in Fig. 5-6. The surfaces outlined by the parallel lines in this sketch represent the isobaric surfaces. The component of the earth's angular velocity, $2\Omega \sin \theta$, generates an acceleration at right angles to the velocity u as indicated in the drawing. If we make use of force balance on a mass of fluid in each section assuming the vertical gradient of pressure is hydrostatic, we find that the pressure distributions are given by:

$$
\begin{aligned}
p_1 &= p_0 - \rho_1 g\, \Delta z - 2\Omega \sin \theta u_1 \rho_1\, \Delta x, \\
p_2 &= p_0 - \rho_2 g\, \Delta z - 2\Omega \sin \theta u_2 \rho_2\, \Delta x,
\end{aligned}
\tag{5.8}
$$

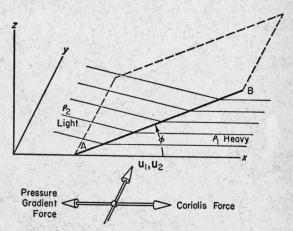

FIG. 5-6 Motion along a surface of discontinuity in density.

where p_0 denotes a reference pressure, and θ is again the angle of latitude. At the surface of discontinuity AB, the pressure will be equal in both fluids, or $p_1 = p_2$. If p_0 is chosen as the reference pressure on the surface of discontinuity, $p_1 = p_2 = p_0$, and the angle that the surface makes with the horizontal direction ϕ can be calculated from Eq. (5.8), or

$$\tan \phi = \frac{\Delta z}{\Delta x} = \frac{2\Omega \sin \theta (u_2 \rho_2 - u_1 \rho_1)}{g(\rho_1 - \rho_2)}. \tag{5.9}$$

This relation, named the *Margules equation* after its discoverer, tells us that density contrasts may exist for different fluids in steady motion next to each other in a rotating system. Further-more, the surface of the density contrast can never be vertically oriented in a real system, but has to lie at some angle ϕ to the horizontal plane. This angle depends on the angle of latitude θ, the density difference, and the relative velocities of the masses of fluid.

Even though our arguments above are somewhat crude, re-markably enough, Eq. (5.9) estimates fairly accurately the aver-age angle ϕ associated with surfaces of discontinuities, or fronts (p. 90), in the atmosphere.

Frontal disturbances are commonly found in the troposphere at the middle latitudes. As remarked earlier in this chapter, their development and properties are related to ageostrophic motion in the meridional circulation as well as to the eddy structure ob-served above 20-30° latitude. A particularly important frontal system develops when warm tropical air masses move poleward and encounter the cold polar air drifting towards the equator. The region of discontinuity associated with this kind of en-counter is called the *polar front*. Its hypothetical position is indi-cated in the middle cell of Fig. 5-3(B).

The simplest model of a front follows from Margules' idealized picture in Fig. 5-6. With primary winds blowing nearly parallel to the surface of discontinuity, warmer air or cooler air may slowly advance on slower moving masses of lower or higher tem-perature. When cool air overtakes warmer air and drifts under-neath it, a *cold front* develops as sketched in Fig. 5-7(A). Warm air slipping over retreating cold air gives rise to a *warm front*,

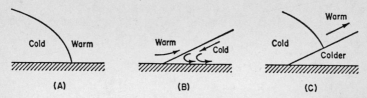

FIG. 5-7 Vertical cross-sections of fronts: (A) cold front, (B) warm front, (C) occluded front.

drawn in Fig. 5-7(B). Cold fronts often travel faster than warm fronts. Therefore, the increased frictional drag acting on a cold front tends to bend the frontal surface somewhat more steeply down to the ground than the more gentle wedge shape of the warm front. Occlusion of fronts may take place when a cold front overtakes a warm front, and the boundary associated with the cold front is forced upward as indicated in Fig. 5-7(C).

To approach conditions of equilibrium, ordinarily we think of flow processes combined with diffusive molecular motions as mechanisms for smoothing out gradients in properties of fluids. One peculiar feature of the behavior of frontal systems suggests that flow of air near the surface of discontinuity may help to steepen horizontal gradients of properties across the front instead of weakening them. If the same particles of air would remain in the region of the discontinuity, the steep gradients in density or temperature gradually diminish by the action of microscale processes. However, when vertical motion of air develops along the front, new air particles continually replace the old ones, and the steep gradients in properties can be depleted or intensified depending on the direction of vertical flow. If, for example, cool air settles as indicated by the arrows in Fig. 5-7(B), the warm front will be maintained or intensified. If circulation exists in the opposite direction, the front will weaken. The case sketched in Fig. 5-7(B) where warm air rises and cold air sinks, is a commonly observed "direct" circulation that leads to the release of potential energy to the kinetic energy of fluid motion.

Because steep gradients in air properties occur in frontal zones, rather intense convective motion frequently develops near these regions. The uplifting of warm air along fronts often results in cloud formation and stormy weather (see also Chapter 7).

Although the exact reasons why the atmosphere tends to maintain sharp density contrasts are not well understood, this behavior often is rationalized, for example, in Chapter 7, by noting that transport of heat and matter is carried more efficiently by moving large masses of air over distances in a "super" eddy rather than by diffusion through fine-scale swirls or molecular processes.

One certainly recognizes from the description of the general circulation that polar and equatorial air do not move meridionally as zonal rings. The tendency for isolated masses of air to move as entities shows up on weather maps as the polar front displays horizontally waving surfaces of discontinuity, characterizing the cold air penetrating equatorward and warm air swirling around the cold outbreaks towards the poles. The long horizontal waves on frontal surfaces reflect, of course, the baroclinic structure of the atmosphere in the mid-latitudes (see also p. 78 and p. 84). The waves can develop from very small perturbations to large amplitude disturbances in a manner which is analogous to the behavior of the discontinuity in Fig. 4-11. Sometimes the frontal waves "break" like ocean waves and form closed circulations called *cyclones*. Cyclonic vortices are discussed in somewhat more detail with other regular eddies in Chapter 7.

Because intense horizontal gradients in air density exist near fronts, one may expect to find the strongest thermal winds appearing in a strip along the frontal waves. In fact the jet stream in the mid-latitudes often seems to be the direct result of amplification of the thermal winds over frontal disturbances. We have noted that the jet stream occurs with maximum velocities near the tropopause. At these altitudes, friction along the ground does not affect the direction of the wind, so that the thermal wind, given by Eq. (4.28), points in a direction normal to the gradients in density. Hence, the high-speed flow of the jet essentially parallels the front at high altitude. These winds reach maximum intensity near the tropopause, as discussed in Chapter 4, because of the decrease in wind speed towards the earth's surface resulting from friction, and because of a reversal in horizontal temperature gradients in the stratosphere.

A typical vertical cross-section of the jet stream is shown in

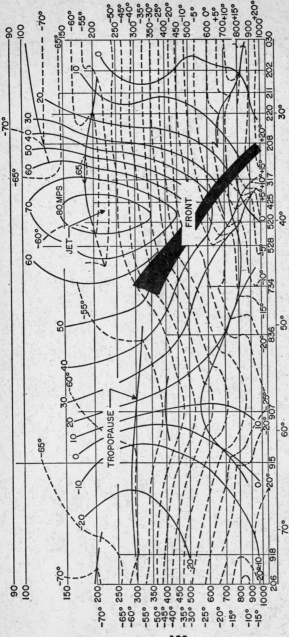

FIG. 5-8 Vertical cross-section of the atmosphere showing the structure of the jet stream. The section is taken on January 17, 1947 along the meridian passing through Thule, Greenland. Vertical lines indicate the position of soundings taken. Solid lines indicate the contours of constant geostrophic wind in meters sec^{-1}. The dashed lines are isotherms in °C. [From E. Palmen's, "On the distribution of temperature and wind in the upper westerlies," J. Meteorol., 5, 23 (1948).]

Fig. 5-8.[3] This section was taken along the meridian passing through Thule, Greenland. It shows the distinct relation between the jet stream, the polar front, and the tropopause. The break in the tropopause in the region of the jet stream and above the front effectively permits air to be exchanged between the troposphere and the stratosphere.

Thus, we see that the jet stream, a streak of high-velocity current, is a natural feature of the baroclinic structure of the atmosphere. The jet lies over the mid-latitudes, flowing westerly on the average, but snakes along with frontal waves and perturbations of the upper-level winds. The connection between the jet stream and thermal convection in a rotating fluid is well demonstrated in the dishpan experiments of the laboratory. One can speculate historically that clever meteorologists well might have discovered the jet had they taken a careful look at Vettin's early laboratory experiments long before World War II.

About the same time that the strong winds at high altitude in the mid-latitudes were observed, concentrated bands of somewhat milder winds were discovered in the high westerlies near the horse latitudes of 30°. These winds, called the *subtropical jet,* are not associated with fronts, but they may have baroclinic origins in that they seem to be related to differences in heating of the atmosphere over continents and over oceans. The subtropical jet also lies in the region which is believed to be the zone of maximum meridional transport of angular momentum at upper levels.

[3] This particular case has certain historical importance. The Finnish meteorologist, E. Palmén used this diagram as the first example of an analysis of the jet stream in which its association with fronts was established. The idea of the jet stream was introduced into meteorology with Palmén's synoptic study in 1947.

6 *Breezes, Bubbles, Wakes and Waves—Some Glimpses of Vertical Currents*

Within the structure of the largest patterns of winds lies a wide variety of interacting vertical currents ranging over length scales of kilometers to less than a centimeter. Atmospheric activity in such size ranges is linked closely to fluctuations in the form of convective motion and wave motion. Disturbances in the vertical structure of the atmosphere occur virtually all of the time at one location or another, or at one zone of altitudes or another in the troposphere. Reflected in this fantastic display of different air currents is the lumpy and sometimes streaky appearance of the atmosphere.

It sometimes is quite difficult to distinguish between convection and wave-like disturbances. Indeed the formal mathematical theory of both kinds of flow has striking similarities. For our purposes, however, it is useful to divide the subsequent sections first into a brief discussion of convective processes, then later into some remarks about waves which are generated inside the troposphere by the action of gravity.

CONVECTIVE CIRCULATION

Convection can take place in the atmosphere either through local differences in air density, brought about by unbalanced heating, or by the action of shearing flow over the earth's surface. The vertical motion induced in the former case is called *natural* or *free convection*. In Chapter 3 we found that free convection arose as a natural consequence of simple ideas of hydrostatic stability. Furthermore, the rate of generation of circulatory motion in a thermally stratified fluid can be estimated by Bjerknes' relation, Eq. (4.7). The discussion in Chapter 4 also suggested how forced convection comes about with the diffusion of vorticity within regions of shearing flow. Thus, whenever there exists unstable layering of air, or regions of shear in the winds, one can expect convective motion to be present in the atmosphere.

Convective Circulation and Sea Breezes. One interesting example of the consequences of initiating natural circulation on horizontal scales of approximately 100 km is involved in the explanation of sea breezes. It is well known along sea coasts that surface winds blow shoreward from the sea by day, while during the night the wind reverses direction to blow from the land towards the water surface. An explanation of this phenomenon lies in the fact that these circulation patterns are initiated under baroclinic conditions in the surface layers of air. Since the land usually becomes warmer than the sea during the day, and since air density decreases upwards, surfaces of constant density, *isopycnics*, will tend to slope upward from land to the sea as shown by the dashed lines in Fig. 6-1. However, the isobaric surfaces tend to remain nearly horizontal so that a baroclinic structure forms locally in the at-

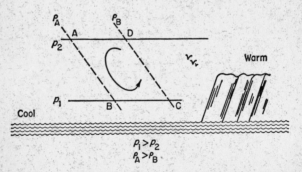

FIG. 6-1 Circulation and the formation of sea breezes.

mosphere. Applying Bjerknes' relation, Eq. (4.7), to the case in Fig. 6-1, we find that the rate of change of circulation is:

$$\frac{d\Gamma}{dt} = - \int_{C=ABCD} \frac{dp}{\rho} = (p_1 - p_2) \left(\frac{1}{\rho_A} - \frac{1}{\rho_B} \right), \qquad (6.1)$$

having chosen as a typical contour the parallelepiped, ABCD. Thus, from considerations of hydrostatic stability, the air over the land will be warmed and will rise. To complete the circulation, cool air sinks to the surface and travels landward from the sea at lower levels, while at upper levels, a return flow develops taking the warm air out over the sea. At night the land cools by radiation while the sea surface remains relatively uniform in temperature because of the large capacity for heat storage in the water. Consequently, the isopycnic surfaces turn around to slope in a direction opposite from those in Fig. 6-1, causing a circulation to appear that produces a land breeze from land to sea near the earth's surface.

The land and sea breezes may be influenced strongly by friction and the earth's rotation. For example, Eq. (6.1) implies that the surface winds along a sea coast would continuously increase in speed during the day. However, friction exerts a braking action on this baroclinic circulation, allowing, theoretically at least, steady winds to develop. If the system of sea breeze circulation is large enough in scale for the Coriolis force to be important, there will be a shifting of the horizontal motion of air out of the vertical plane in Fig. 6-1. That is, the landward bound air would gain a component coming out of the page, while seaward moving air would tend to swing into the page.

The condition shown in Fig. 6-1 constitutes a *direct solenoidal circulation,* one in which potential energy is converted to kinetic energy [see also the circulation in Fig. 5-7(B)]. An indirect circulation results in energy conversion in the opposite direction to the case shown in Fig. 6-1.

The Structure of Natural Convection and Atmospheric Disturbances. Many photographs like Plate II taken at high altitude have revealed very distinctive streaked or cellular patterns of clouds on horizontal scales of about 100 km. Since Sir J. Thomson's identification in 1882 of natural convection with cellular flow in layers of liquid, meteorologists have been tempted to connect regularities in air motion with convective cells. As early as 1885, Friedrich Vettin discussed this possibility, and performed some unique laboratory experiments intended to model structures of cirro-cumulus clouds.

To illustrate the characteristics of natural convection, it is interesting to retrace some simple experiments carried out at the turn of the century by Henri Bénard, for whom regular convection cells have been named. Bénard found that heating of a thin layer of water in a pan very slowly and uniformly over a burner produced different kinds of thermal circulations. Initially, under the simultaneous influence of thermal conduction and friction in the liquid, it was possible to maintain for a time a motionless state with density increasing with height. If, however, the difference between the surface temperature of the liquid and the temperature at the bottom of the pan exceeded a certain value, upward and downward currents began to appear. This circulation began irregularly, but soon there was a transition to a rather regular subdivision of the liquid into cells, as sketched in Fig. 6-2. As the temperature difference reached a value only slightly larger than critical, the cells became arranged into hexagonal (Fig. 6-2) or square honeycomb-like structures. The liquid tended to rise in the center of the cells, and to fall near the boundaries. For

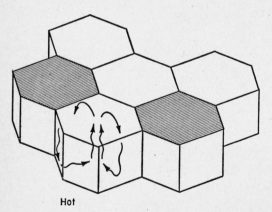

Hot

FIG. 6-2 Cellular convection.

larger vertical differences in temperature or greater depths of liquid, the cells broke down into less regular, but still stable structures. Still higher temperature differences produced an unsteady irregular flow which displayed the characteristics of turbulence. The results of Bénard's experiments indicated that the beginning of cellular convection depends on the balance buoyancy forces and dissipative factors, heat conduction and friction.

Recalling the discussion on pp. 40-42, the buoyancy force per unit mass is proportional to $g(\rho_1 - \rho_2)\rho_{av}$, where subscripts 1 and 2 refer to the bottom and top of the fluid layer. The average density ρ_{av} is the arithmetic average of ρ_1 and ρ_2, equal to ρ_1, approximately, for small differences in temperature. It seems reasonable to expect that thermal circulation should appear in a fluid when the buoyancy force exceeds some parameter identified with the dissipative components. A force per unit mass has dimensions of $[\text{length}][\text{time}]^{-2}$. A characteristic number having the same dimensions, made up of the properties associated with thermal conduction and friction is $\kappa v/d^3$, where κ is the thermal diffusivity of the fluid, equal to the ratio of the thermal conductivity to the product of the fluid density times its specific heat, v is the kinematic viscosity of the fluid, μ/ρ, and d is the height of the fluid. Experiments on fluid systems with a rigid boundary on the bottom, and a free surface on top, have indicated that if the ratio of "forces,"

$$Ra = \frac{g(\rho_1 - \rho_2)d^3}{\kappa v \rho_{av}} \qquad (6.2)$$

exceeds a critical value of about 1200, regular cellular convection will begin. The transition to irregular, chaotic turbulent motion takes place when Ra becomes approximately 47,000.

Lord Rayleigh in 1916 first related the ratio in Eq. (6.2) to the onset of convective instability; therefore, this ratio has been named for him.

Convective cells also can appear in fluids undergoing shear. In this case the cellular circulation becomes superimposed on the average flow, and consequently the closed hexagonal honeycombs can be stretched out into parallel rolls along the direction of shear, as sketched in Fig. 6-3. Adjacent cells rotate in opposite

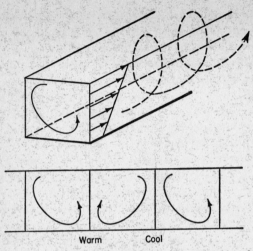

FIG. 6-3 Cellular convection and shearing flow—helical circulation.

directions so that, ideally, fluid particles move around neighboring helical spirals in a manner somewhat similar to the Bénard circulation.

Workers have speculated that the meso-scale patterns of clouds in the atmosphere are associated with cells that are analogous to Bénard cells when there is no wind shear. An example of a quasi-cellular structure marked by clouds is shown in a photo taken from Tiros VIII satellite [Plate II(B)]. Other cells may be drawn out into spiralling streaks with the wind direction when shear exists, as for example revealed by tropical cumuli in Plate II(A).

Analogies of this kind involve an extrapolation of convection mechanisms for the slow, small-scale laminar flows in the laboratory to behavior in the highly turbulent[1] atmosphere where the motion is much faster, occurring on scales about 10^6 larger, and the rate of heating with its spatial distribution of air is considerably different from the idealized experiments. Therefore, the details of the dynamics of regular cell-like circulation in the atmosphere cannot be the same as the laboratory analogies even though the phenomena qualitatively look alike. In all fairness to

[1] For example, a typical Rayleigh number for meso-scale motion ($L \sim 100$ km) is about 10^{10} for the atmosphere.

the laboratory analogies, however, the relative simplicity of controlled experimentation certainly can lead to many new ideas and improved conceptual theories which may be very useful for better understanding the physical processes causing the complicated patterns of atmospheric motion. This point may be illustrated very well by taking a closer look at the convection associated with a single cumulus cloud in the many illustrated in Plate II.

Thermals. When the growth of a rising cumulus cloud is observed, one gets the impression that this system behaves very much like a smoke plume jetting from a stack on a calm day, or a bubble of vapor rising from the bottom of a tea pot containing slowly boiling water. Thus for example, the progress of a convective element through the atmosphere [e.g., Plate I(A)] can be pictured ideally in terms of lumps of hot air, called *thermals,* departing from a localized source of heat on the earth's surface. Vertical velocities in such "bubbles" of air can range from a few tenths of meters per second to several meters per second depending on the intensity of heating at the surface. As the thermal advances upward, it mixes with surrounding air and becomes larger, as sketched in Fig. 6-4(B). After some time, most of the fluid contained in a thermal has entered from the surroundings. There-

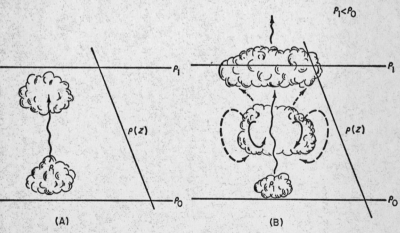

FIG. 6-4 Development of penetrative convection: (A) no mixing, (B) with mixing.

fore, the thermal's momentum and vorticity will have been induced largely by the buoyancy forces acting on the fluid.

Once the bubble analogy to cumulus convection was recognized, scientists devised some ingenious laboratory experiments to study the details of motion in idealized thermals. Through the 1950s and 1960s, the work of R. S. Scorer and his colleagues at Imperial College in England represents some of the first attempts to develop analogies to cumulus convection. Their experiments consisted simply of dumping a salt solution into a large tank of water. The spreading of the salt solution gave a qualitative picture of the turbulent motion associated with a (negatively) buoyant bubble. When, for example, a solution of barium chloride was released in a tank of water containing a little sodium sulphate, a chemical reaction occurred which forms a dense white precipitate of barium sulphate. The movement of the precipitate downward and outward demonstrated graphically how an idealized thermal grows (Plate IX). The progress of the thermal is downward, of course, in this experiment because the barium chloride solution is heavier than pure water. The situation is reversed in the atmosphere, where lumps of warm air rise and form cumulus clouds as water vapor begins to condense out of the air. Note how the billowy bottom of the laboratory thermal develops in Plate IX. This is strikingly similar to the upper regions of cumulus clouds in the atmosphere, as pictured in Plate I.

The laboratory studies of thermals have produced a picture of a thermal as a mass of buoyant fluid advancing in such a way that the thermal grows in radius linearly with vertical distance. The thermal's central core moves most rapidly relative to the whole thermal. In the core of an atmospheric thermal, the vertical velocity then has an upward direction. Between the core and the surrounding fluid, where the density changes are large, the air is forced downwards, as indicated earlier in Fig. 4-7. The denser air around the outer portions of the thermal is then carried around to the rear so that the lighter core is forced to rise within the thermal as a result of the action of the buoyancy force. Then a ring of vorticity is induced. As buoyant fluid rises, the isopycnics would tend to slope upwards towards the core of the thermal while the isobars would remain more nearly horizontal. Thus, further ap-

plication of Bjerknes' relation, Eq. (4.7), indicates that vorticity
in the thermal must be generated continuously with circulation
in the direction that was shown in Fig. 4-7.

Careful observations of the laboratory thermals sinking down
into the tank of water indicated that mixing of surrounding fluid
takes place mainly at the "cap" at the bottom of the precipitate
cloud in Plate IX (the top of an ideal cumulus cloud). Mixing of
buoyant air in a cloud with the surrounding air must proceed
then largely through the formation of turbulent bubble-like pro-
jections which act as small thermals superimposed on the larger
one. Air that is not mixed into the thermal is pushed aside by the
rising bubble, and flows smoothly around into the tail of the
vortex system. As a result of the mixing processes, buoyancy in the
advancing core becomes smaller, and, as the volume of fluid containing vorticity increases, the fluid velocities in the thermal tend
to decrease steadily.

Recalling the ideas of hydrostatic instability in Chapter 3 to
describe the behavior of a rising isolated element of air, we recog-
nize that the introduction of mixing complicates somewhat the
original picture of buoyant motion of air. Suppose we consider the
case in Fig. 6-4(A). An element of warm air of density ρ_1 is rising
through a region of linearly decreasing density $\rho(z)$ in the surroundings. Since the acceleration of the element is proportional
to $\rho_1 - \rho(z)$, it will advance upwards without mixing at a speed
decreasing with height. At a height z_1 corresponding to ρ_1, the
element's acceleration will be zero. If, however, there is mixing of
heavier air from the surroundings as indicated in Fig. 6-4(B), the
buoyant element's vertical velocity will be less than the case in
which no mixing occurs because its buoyancy per unit volume decreases. On the other hand, if fluid from the surroundings is
mixed into a rising element which is lighter than the core of the
element, its buoyancy force per unit volume increases, and the
element can move upwards faster than the case of an unmixed
parcel. Observations of actual cloud elements in the atmosphere
have indicated that it is necessary to incorporate mixing to explain their growth and rate of rise.

Buoyancy can be generated in an element of a convective cloud
even though it ascends through regions of heavier air because of

heat liberated during condensation of water vapor. Conversely evaporation in a cloud gives rise to a negative buoyancy which tends to erode away the cloudy thermal. Erosion occurs because vorticity is produced from evaporative cooling which tends to rotate in a sense opposing that sketched in Fig. 4-7 and Fig. 6-4(B).

When a spot on the ground is warmed locally, heat is transferred away from the spot with the formation and rise of air in a bubble-like thermal. If this heated zone on the surface is not maintained, the single thermal may remove enough energy from the spot to attain conditions of equilibrium at the surface. However, when the zones of local heating remain, a sequence of bubbles can rise from the source. If the train of thermals is produced rapidly enough, a steady upward flow at the source may develop giving a plume-like jet.

The conceptual analogies of cumulus convection of bubble-like thermals and plumes are very closely related. In fact the top of a plume qualitatively tends to mix with surrounding air like a cap of a rising thermal. The main difference between these two simple models lies in the effective rate of mixing of surrounding air into regions of the upward flow. Laboratory experiments have shown that the bubble model tends to spread horizontally about three times faster with altitude than the plume. Recent observations of cumulus clouds have suggested that these convective systems in the atmosphere may behave like a combination plume and a bubble, with spreading more like a plume.

Generation of Sources for Thermal Convection. Although thermals can appear in air of non-uniform density circulating over perfectly uniform terrain, the nature of surface roughness may help to generate these more or less isolated systems of rising air. Wind blowing over bumps in topography can force thermal convection to begin in regions of unstably stratified air. Differences in air density can develop over localized regions of warm and cool ground. The local variation in temperature of the earth's surface emerges in several ways. If sunlight ceases to fall on the ground because of the shadow of clouds, or if cool air above an unstable layer sinks and locally spreads out over the surface, relatively cool areas surrounded by warmer zones will form on the terrain. Furthermore, sun-facing slopes have been found to become warmer than the surrounding land as a result of receiving more total radiation than flat surfaces do, and settled communities can easily act as artificial sources of heat. On the other hand, irrigated regions can be cooler than adjacent topography because of the evaporation of water.

Winds blowing across continuous sources of heat such as manu-facturing plants may produce lines of thermals arranged parallel to the winds, which have been called *thermal streets*. Lines of cumulus clouds like those in Plate II(A) may be associated with thermal streets induced by local temperature differences in water near the ocean's surface. Strong contrasts in surface temperature are more likely to develop at the ground than on water because thermal gradients tend to be smoothed out by turbulent mixing in the ocean. Hence, other mechanisms such as instability in shearing flow of air may be involved in forming the lines of cumuli in Plate II(A) (See also p. 120).

Deserts are particularly suitable places to find sources for thermals. Diurnal changes in surface temperature in these arid regions can range over 70°C or more. The exceedingly high tem-peratures at the ground during the day can cause large unstable lapse rates. Consequently, layers of unstable air frequently extend higher over the deserts than over other places. Even though strong convective activity in desert regions exists, it sometimes may not be observed because the ascending air near the ground contains too little water vapor for formation of clouds.

On land, surface temperatures tend to rise fairly uniformly in the morning and in the early afternoon, but decrease at night with radiation loss from the ground to the atmosphere. In con-trast, the temperature of the sea remains nearly constant for depths of several meters. Because of the large capacity for heat storage in water and the mixing processes near the surface, the oceans reveal relatively little variation in surface temperature be-tween day and night. Therefore, the air over bodies of water is frequently more stable than over land during the day, but air is sometimes less stable than over land at night. Since there are no isolated sources of strong heating on the oceans, convection of air over water often seems to take place through many small thermals like those in Plate II(A) rather than by a few large ones. Clouds may become larger over the oceans even though the air is more stable than over land during the day because the convective processes can operate more or less continuously during both day and night.

Recent observations of convective activity suggest that there is often little correlation between sources for convection on the ground, and the appearance of cumulus clouds. That is, a concentrated updraft induced at the surface as a plume or a bubble may not strictly maintain its identity during its rise through cloud base several hundred meters above. Thus, these simple conceptual models of thermal convection do not provide the complete picture of cumulus convection in the atmosphere.

FORCED CONVECTION AND BOUNDARY LAYERS

The passage of fluid over a solid boundary causes the formation of a shear layer, which results from the influence of friction between the surface and the fluid, and between layers of fluid just above the surface. If an initially uniform flow moves steadily over a boundary as in Fig. 6-5, a discontinuity analogous to the half of

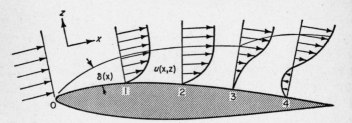

FIG. 6-5   Development of shearing flow in a boundary layer over a curved surface.

the region of ideally infinite shear in Fig. 4-11(A) develops, giving rise to a zone of discontinuity which tends to be spread out by the frictional diffusion of vorticity. As the fluid moves steadily over the boundary, convective motion is forced to develop in the shearing layer by the action of friction. We can demonstrate this effect by applying the principle of continuity. Considering only a two-dimensional slice along the vertical coordinate z, as in Fig. 6-5, we can have vertical divergence or convergence only if there is corresponding horizontal convergence or divergence along x. Thus in this case, the equation of continuity can be written for steady flow in differential form as:

$$\left(\frac{\partial \rho u}{\partial x}\right) + \left(\frac{\partial \rho w}{\partial z}\right) = 0. \tag{6.3}$$

For incompressible flow, $\rho =$ constant, and the change in horizontal velocity u then must be balanced by a negative change in the vertical velocity w. In Fig. 6-5, the horizontal velocity changes downstream with x as the boundary layer grows, say from location 1 to location 2. Thus, at a given distance z from the surface, taken at position 1 and 2, u decreases with x. Over a differential distance along the surface, say δx, as shown in Fig. 6-6, u decreases say by

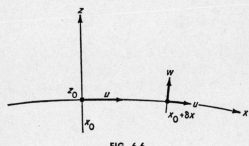

FIG. 6-6

0.1 cm sec^{-1} cm^{-1}. The vertical velocity w then must increase by the same amount according to Eq. (6.3), as illustrated in Fig. 6-6. Therefore, if the component of velocity w is zero at x_0, z_0, then it must be 0.1 cm sec^{-1} at $x_0 + \delta x, z_0$. We may use arguments similar to these to infer that convective motion in the atmosphere can be forced into existence in association with the diffusion of vorticity in a shearing layer near the ground.

Separation. Convective disturbances also may emerge from the influence of pressure increases along the direction of flow. If such a pressure gradient exists in air moving over a boundary sketched, for example, in Fig. 6-5, the entire fluid motion is slowed down. Fluid particles moving slowly in regions close to the surface may eventually stop and reverse their direction of flow even though the fluid farther away from the surface continues to maintain its original direction of motion, as suggested at points 3 and 4, Fig. 6-5. Downstream of location 3, the fluid outside the boundary layer still has sufficient kinetic energy to continue downstream. However, in this zone, more and more fluid in layers away from the solid surface begin to slow down from loss of energy in working against friction and against an (adverse) pressure gradient which is positive in the downstream direction. As the vertical extent of the zone of reversed motion increases, the uniform external flow recedes farther away from the boundary. The reversal of flow in the boundary layer, called *separation*, is accompanied by the sharp thickening of the layer, and the formation of a closed circulation in fluid near the surface. This implies larger vertical velocities will appear with the onset of separation. In the region of flow reversal, an unstable velocity pattern similar to Fig. 4-11 may form, causing vortices to appear in the flowing fluid downstream from the point of separation.

Flow often becomes separated in the lee of obstacles such as houses, rocks, or mountains (e.g., Fig. 6-7). The reversal in flow

FIG. 6-7 Separation of flow behind a house.

in these cases arises because a pressure gradient opposing the downstream motion develops to the leeward of the obstacles. This effect may be deduced easily by applying the principle of continuity and Bernoulli's equation. For example, in the case of steady flow over the mountain in Fig. 5-5(A), the requirement that the disturbance caused by the mountain reach only finite height leads to acceleration of air at the crest of the mountain because the area through which the fluid passes is constricted. Downstream from the obstacle the cross-sectional area for flow returns to a larger size, and the air must decelerate to its original speed far upstream of the mountain. Application of Bernoulli's equation,

Eq. (4.14), then shows that the total pressure along a streamline to the lee of the mountain must be greater than that at the crest.

As the flow of air becomes separated from obstacles, the vortices develop behind the body, shed away and form a trail behind in a sheet called a *wake*. The wake to the lee of a house is sketched in Fig. 6-7. The eddying motion behind obstacles induces large vertical velocities, and results in much stronger convection than streamline flow over a smooth boundary.

Convective Motion and the Reynolds Number. As in the case of natural convection, the intensity of forced convection is closely related to the relative strength of forces controlling fluid motion. When layers of fluid move smoothly in a *laminar* fashion over a boundary, convection is forced to develop to a much less degree than under conditions where eddies are generated. In a homogeneous fluid, the transition from streamline flow to turbulent eddying motion depends on the ratio of the inertial forces and the dissipative viscous forces. On dimensional grounds, the inertial force per unit mass is proportional to the ratio of the square of a velocity U, and a length L characterizing the geometry of flow. From Eq. (4.17), the viscous force per unit mass, on the other hand, is proportional to U/L^2. Hence, the ratio of these two forces, for an element of fluid is:

$$Re = \frac{\rho U^2}{L} \div \frac{\mu U}{L^2} = \frac{\rho UL}{\mu}. \qquad (6.4)$$

This important parameter is named the *Reynolds number* after its discoverer, Sir O. Reynolds.

The choice of the characteristic parameters in Eq. (6.4) often is arbitrary. For example, in the case of steady flow over a mountain, one might choose the velocity U as the geostrophic wind speed, and the length L as the height of the mountain. For flow in a boundary layer, U is usually the free stream value, and with no characteristic geometrical length, L is chosen as the thickness of the boundary layer, δ.

When the Reynolds number is small, on the order of unity, the frictional force dominates the flow. But when the Reynolds number is large, the inertial force controls the fluid motion. If a fluid is homogeneous and the Coriolis force is small, the fluid in a regime of low Reynolds number will respond only to pressure differences, friction, and to the boundaries confining the flow. When pressure differences are increased, the frictional force increases proportionally. Although the inertial force also increases, it still may be very small compared with the other two forces so that the pattern of motion can remain the same for a range of small Re. However, as the Re gets still larger, the inertial force has to become increasingly important, and the characteristics of flow may change markedly even in the same geometrical configuration. For example, at low Re, there can be streamline flow around an obstacle, and no separation. At higher Re, the flow separates, and various vortex patterns will form behind the obstacle, which will change with Re. As the Re grows very large, the bulk of the fluid will behave as if it were frictionless. Frictional effects will be confined to the thin layer in the region very close to geometrical boundaries.

When the Re becomes sufficiently large, the fluid motion even over smooth boundaries may develop irregular, eddying patterns at any instant that are superimposed on an average structure of flow which remains essentially the same. This region governed by very high Re consists of a regime of *turbulent flow*.

The condition of transition from laminar flow to turbulent flow of a homogeneous fluid passing over a smooth flat plate depends on the Reynolds number based on the thickness of the boundary layer, Re_δ. Flow over a flat, smooth surface reflects the amplification of tiny disturbances in the fluid motion at $Re_\delta \approx$ 400-1000. These minute ripples, called *Tollmien-Schlichting waves,* break down into truly turbulent eddies at somewhat higher values of Re_δ. In the atmosphere, Re_δ is ordinarily always much larger than 100 so that the planetary boundary layer displays the characteristics of fully turbulent motion. Some features of turbulence are discussed further in Chapter 8.

Wave-like instabilities also have been observed in the transition of Ekman boundary layers from laminar motion to turbulent motion. The structure of these modes of instability has led meteorologists like Alan Faller at the University of Maryland to associate them with convection in long rows of cumuli like those in Plate II(A), and in spiral bands of clouds in hurricanes. The motion of fluid particles in waves growing in a shear layer looks very similar to the circulation that develops by thermal convection. Previously, we have suggested that the cellular convection in the regularly spaced cloud lines might be the result of thermal effects. At present, there is not enough information about the atmosphere on scales of 10 km or less to determine which of these two mechanisms may be more important in forming the different modes of cell-like convective motion. It is likely, however, that the bands of clouds in the atmosphere have thermal origins rather than frictional origins in most cases.

Since the atmosphere consists of stratified layers of air, vertical motion can result from a combination of thermal effects and frictional effects. At times, of course, one or the other of these mechanisms may control convection. For example, forced convection can dominate only in cases where the air approaches homogeneity in density, or where the hydrostatic stability of the air, $S \geqslant 0$. When $S < 0$ and the wind speed near the ground is small, convection may depend primarily on thermal effects.

ATMOSPHERIC WAVES INDUCED BY BODY FORCES

Perhaps no other phenomenon is as common to all of nature as waves. The atmosphere provides a rather fertile breeding ground for various kinds of wave phenomena. As we have seen, waves may develop in the global westerly flow of air, acoustic waves have become well known particularly in this age of the sonic boom from aircraft traveling at high speeds in the atmosphere, and wave-like disturbances may appear in flow associated with shearing layers. One particular class of waves that forms in the atmosphere depends predominantly on gravity and its action on stratified masses of moving air.

Modes of vertical oscillation set off by various perturbations and propagated by gravity may travel for very long distances before damping out. The origin of these *internal waves* relies on non-homogeneities in density. Therefore, their speed of propagation c, relative to the mass flow of air, then depends on the density contrast between fluid layers, $(\rho_2 - \rho_1)/\rho_{av}$ in addition to a characteristic length L, and gravity. The wave speed c has dimensions of [length][time]$^{-1}$, and we can determine that the simple combination

$$\left[\frac{gL(\rho_2 - \rho_1)}{\rho_{av}}\right]^{1/2}$$

has the same dimensions. Therefore on dimensional grounds, the wave speed should be proportional to this ratio. Indeed, in cases where sinusoidal waves of infinitesimal amplitude and length λ travel over a flat surface in a stratified fluid of layer depth d,

$$c = \left[\frac{g\lambda(\rho_2 - \rho_1)}{\pi\rho_{av}}\right]^{1/2}, \tag{6.5}$$

when the ratio $d/\lambda > 0.05$. However, if the waves are very long and $d/\lambda < 0.05$, the speed becomes dependent on the depth d and not λ:

$$c = \left[\frac{gd(\rho_2 - \rho_1)}{\rho_{av}}\right]^{1/2}. \tag{6.6}$$

Hence, for a given density contrast, the longer the wave length the faster a disturbance can travel. In the longest internal waves, their propagation becomes independent of wave length.

Atmospheric Tides. An important example of internal waves in the atmosphere having exceedingly long wave lengths arises from tidal forces in a manner similar to tides that are generated in the oceans. Tidal oscillations in the atmosphere consist of small perturbations in vertical air motion which are reflected as tiny regular pressure undulations that have periods of oscillation related to the solar day, or to the lunar day, which differs somewhat from the solar day.[2] These pressure disturbances generally have such small amplitudes that they are masked by much larger fluctuations in pressure coming from the instantaneous motion of the atmosphere. However, extremely careful analysis of records of barometric pressure taken over very long periods of time has shown that a regular pattern of semi-diurnal oscillations can be extracted from the random variations in atmospheric pressure at the earth's surface. The existence of atmospheric tides was first

[2] For further details, see, for example, G. Abell, *Exploration of the Universe* (Holt, Rinehart & Winston, New York, 1964), Chapters 6 and 8.

confirmed many years ago from data taken near the equator where the irregularities in barometric pressure caused by local disturbances are weak enough not to strongly mask the tidal fluctuations. Later, with better techniques for analysis, the tidal oscillations were discovered in records obtained at stations in the middle latitudes, where the irregular fluctuations in surface pressure superimposed on the minute tidal regularities are much larger in magnitude. In the patterns of tidal oscillations at both latitudes, pronounced maxima have been found to occur with periods of 12 hours solar time.

The simplest purely gravitational theory of tides relates these oscillations to tidal forces resulting from local differences between gravitational forces exerted on two bodies near the earth by a third more distant body. Consider, for example, two spherical elements of air at the same altitude as indicated in Fig. 6-8(A).

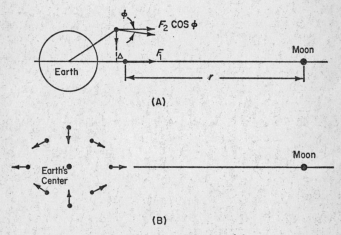

FIG. 6-8 Idealized picture of tidal forces.

The mass of the moon acts to pull these spherules slightly away from the earth. From Newton's law of gravitation, the horizontal component of the gravitational force of the moon on element 1, F_1, is proportional to M/r^2, where M is the mass of the moon, and r is the distance between the element and the center of mass of the moon. Since element 2 is slightly farther away from the moon, the horizontal component of the moon's gravitational force F_2 acting on it is proportional to:

$$F_2 \propto \frac{M \cos \phi}{(r + \Delta)^2}.$$

Because the angle ϕ is very small, $\cos \phi \approx 1$, and the difference between the force acting on 1 and 2 is very nearly proportional to:

$$F_1 - F_2 = \delta F \propto M \left[\frac{1}{r^2} - \frac{1}{(r + \Delta)^2} \right]. \qquad (6.7)$$

The far right side of Eq. (6.7) reduces to the approximate value

$$\delta F \propto \frac{2M\Delta}{r^3} \qquad (6.8)$$

by taking into account that $r \gg \Delta$. Thus the tidal force acting on elements of air is proportional to the mass of the distant body, say the moon or the sun, but inversely proportional to the cube of the distance from the earth to the body.

When the *vector differences* between the attractive force acting on an element of air and an element located at the center of the earth are accounted for, we find as drawn in Fig. 6-8(B) that particles of air at right angles to the line between centers of mass of the moon and the earth are pushed inwards, while particles oriented along the line centers are bulged outwards. Consequently, local differences in gravitational forces ideally cause the atmosphere to have a maximum depth along the line between the centers of mass of the earth and the distant body, and minimum depth at points perpendicular to this line. The same sort of reasoning, of course, applies to the gravitational interaction between the sun and the earth's atmosphere.

The moon's mass is only $1/80$ of the earth's in contrast to the sun's mass, which is $3 \cdot 10^5$ times the earth's mass. However, because the sun is 400 times farther away from the earth than the moon, we see from Eq. (6.8) that the lunar tide should dominate the atmosphere if the tides have purely gravitational origins. Therefore, as found in the oceans, one would expect maxima appearing in the tidal oscillations of barometric pressure ideally in half a lunar day rather than half a solar day as is observed.

Since the oceanic tides are known to be closely related to the lunar day, the atmospheric tides must be connected to other effects besides differences in gravitational attraction. Non-gravitational theories for tidal phenomena came about as early as 1799 with an idea of Pierre Laplace, who proposed that tides in the atmosphere could have thermal origins induced by periodicity in incident sunlight. Later in 1882, Lord Kelvin suggested that a particular harmonic of thermally generated tides should be amplified by resonance. By the 1930s the resonance theory of tides was refined and extended by Sydney Chapman and others.

Although certain recent measurements of pressure oscillations, especially at high altitudes, have cast some doubts on the details of the early resonance theory, scientists still believe that tidal phenomena in the atmosphere result from a combination of the influences of gravity and thermal effects involving diurnal changes in solar heating.

Lee Waves. Internal waves of smaller lengths than tidal waves can originate in the atmosphere from many kinds of perturbations. One particularly interesting example is the stationary waves of lengths of a kilometer or larger that are generated when stratified air moves over mountains. The existence of these waves can often be determined by regularly spaced bands of lenticular clouds running to the lee of and nearly parallel to mountain ranges as sketched in Fig. 6-9. The lines of clouds form as air rises

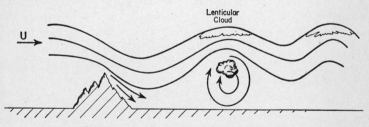

FIG. 6-9 Lee waves forming behind a mountain.

to the crests of waves. These clouds tend to form at 5-10 km above the mountains and have sharp curved upper boundaries picturing the wave crest. An example of such a cloud east of the Sierra Nevada range in California is shown in Plate IV.

As lee waves form behind mountains, their amplitude may become rather large. Under some conditions, the vertical and horizontal motion associated with the lee wave may be sufficiently large that separation may occur in the frictional layer along the ground. If the air flow separates, a large closed eddy called a *rotor* may appear under the crest of a wave (Fig. 6-9). Indications of rotors have been observed in the lee of the Rocky Mountains, the Alps, and behind mountains near Cumberland, England. A spectacular example of this phenomenon has been explored using gliders in the Owens Valley in California. Here the Sierra Nevada Mountains rise about 2000 meters from the floor of the Owens Valley. The rotor that frequently forms to the lee of the Sierras in the valley has been observed to be as large as 3 to 6 km in diameter. A cloud making this rotor visible is seen below the lenticular clouds in Plate IV. The fuzzy, eddying structure of this rotor cloud pictures the highly turbulent nature of the rotor, as contrasted to the smooth flow over the crest of the waves.

The formation of gravity waves behind mountain ridges depends on the characteristics of air motion as determined primarily by the ratio of the inertial force to the buoyancy force:

$$Fr = \frac{U}{\left[\dfrac{g(\rho_2 - \rho_1)d}{\rho_{av}}\right]^{1/2}}, \qquad (6.9)$$

where U again denotes a characteristic horizontal velocity. The ratio Fr has a long history of interest to workers in hydraulics. In fact, the significance of this parameter was discovered a century ago by the English engineer William Froude during his research of water flow in open channels.

If the Froude number is very small, the body force controls air motion, but flow behind obstacles is quite irregular, displaying jets, and small vortices with relatively little vertical motion. However, at values of Fr approximately unity, the large amplitude stationary waves form behind obstacles. For example, three lee waves are observed in the Owens Valley for $Fr \approx 0.1$. When Fr becomes approximately 0.2, the well known one-wave case develops with the rotor forming under the crest of the wave.

A successful hydrodynamic model of the Owens Valley wave

system, executed by Robert Long of the Johns Hopkins University, verified the fact that the Froude number substantially controls lee wave phenomena. To duplicate the atmospheric prototype, Long steadily towed a little model of the Owens Valley-Sierra Nevada topography through a tank containing water stably stratified with salt solution. He observed both the three-wave case and the one-wave formation at approximately the values of the Froude number found for these conditions in the atmosphere. One of these cases is shown in Plate X. The flow over the model is traced by aluminum particles in the water. The appearance of the waves, and the rotor, show up beautifully in the experiments.

From the streaks in Plate X, one can identify rather strong downslope winds on the leeward slope of mountains accompanying the formation of the lee wave. Such downslope flow can reach speeds as high as 40 meter sec^{-1}, and may be concentrated in a few meters height or may become part of the entire airstream. These winds are observed occasionally at the foot of the Eastern slope of the Rocky Mountains. When the downslope winds build up, they tend to make life rather unpleasant for the local residents, especially for those who have large glass windows to view the majestic peaks to the west.

7 Eddies—Concentrated, Regular Vertices

Imbedded in the great currents of the atmosphere are myriads of swirls containing spinning air. The eddying motion develops on scales ranging in diameter from hundreds of kilometers to less than a millimeter. On length scales larger than tens of meters, the rotating flow occasionally makes an identifiable appearance as horizontally oriented circulations like a cyclonic storm or a tornado in the mid-latitudes, or a hurricane or a typhoon in the tropics.[1] On smaller scales, the swirling motion tends to be ever present in the wind structure, but has much less spectacular consequences on our lives than the larger, more persistent eddies. If the eddying has a random distribution in time and space as usually occurs in the atmosphere, the flow is regarded as being *turbulent*.

Depending on one's point of view, or on the time scales being considered, the eddies may be examined as statistically defined secondary disturbances of a primary pattern of instantaneous flow (see also p. 91), or the swirls themselves may be studied as identifiable lumps of spinning fluid traveling individually within a large current. In this chapter we shall confine our attention to the latter case, and we shall describe certain features of the origins and behavior of more or less regular eddies having diameters

[1] Hurricanes and typhoons are both tropical cyclones having essentially the same mechanistic origins. Storms beginning over the Atlantic Ocean normally are referred to as the former, while Pacific storms are the latter (see also p. 132).

greater than about 10 meters. These masses of concentrated spinning motion ordinarily persist long enough to be identified within the local wind structure for matters of minutes or longer. Later, in Chapter 8 we shall examine some important properties of eddying motion in the light of the theory of turbulence. Particular emphasis in the last section will be placed on air motion over length scales less than 10 meters, where eddies play a truly secondary role in the fluid flow as we understand it from our everyday experience with turbulent media in the laboratory.

EXTRATROPICAL CYCLONES

Cyclonic disturbances emerging in the winds of the mid-latitudes are the largest vortices that occur in the atmosphere. As noted in Chapter 5 they ordinarily develop with the meanderings of frontal surfaces traveling eastward across the earth. Typically their diameter reaches as large as 1500 km, with maximum winds of about 20 meter sec^{-1}. Cyclones are familiar features on weather maps. They tend to be unsymmetrical horizontally, often elliptical in shape with the major axis oriented towards the north-south direction. As indicated in Fig. 4-16, it is not unusual to find two or three of these vortices moving around a hemisphere at any given time.

Meteorologists have to watch the formation and movements of cyclones rather carefully because of the stormy weather that accompanies these disturbances. Cyclonic storms make their presence known particularly in the winter months when they cause large amounts of precipitation to fall upon the earth.

Many years ago atmospheric scientists recognized that cyclonic circulations develop in regions where contrasts in air density are quite large. Using this observation, the Scandinavian school of meteorologists led by J. Bjerknes began to formulate the *polar front theory of cyclones* early in the twentieth century. Much of our present knowledge about these giant vortices stems from the work of this group. According to the polar front theory, cyclones develop in connection with wave formation along frontal surfaces. The waves appear as a result of the influence of perturbations in the wind field, which may arise from the combination of disturbing influences of mountain ranges (p. 95), from sudden changes in surface friction at coastlines, from temperature contrasts between oceans and the continents, or from the effects of developments in low pressure near the tropopause. Once a wave appears along the front, it may increase in amplitude until large volumes of polar air and tropical air are swept away from their origins, eventually to be modified and mixed together, or the wave may remain small in amplitude and die away without contributing to meridional transport of air. When a frontal disturbance becomes unstable because of peculiar distributions of air flow, temperature and humidity, the initial perturbation will grow in amplitude until it breaks like a wave on the ocean's surface. As the break occurs over several hours or many days, the air in trying to adjust to equilibrium pushes inward towards this weakness along the front. Under the combination of gradient wind conditions, and the action of friction, as described in Chapter 4, cyclonic circulation develops around the crest of the frontal wave.

The picture of cyclone formation looks similar to the development of vortices along discontinuities in velocity shown in Fig. 4-11. In Fig. 7-1, *cyclogenesis* is sketched for a case in the Northern Hemisphere. On the front separating the polar easterlies and the westerlies, an unstable wave appears [Fig. 7-1(A)]. In Fig. 7-1(B), the westerlies swing into a southwest gradient wind that presses the eastern "warm" portion of the front to the north, and sucks the western part southward as a cold front. Instead of rolling over in the direction of propagation eastward like a water wave, the fronts become convex towards the direction of their movement.

Considering the remarks on p. 101, we observe that the cold front travels faster than the warm front, closing the sector to form an occlusion as indicated in Fig. 7-1(C). This constitutes an overlapping of the frontal surfaces in such a way that the warm region of air is closed off from the surface and is forced aloft as shown in Fig. 5-7(C). As occlusion continues, the warm sector is pushed upwards and the circulation at the surface becomes surrounded entirely by cold air. Then the two masses of air involved along the original front in Fig. 7-1(A) become modified com-

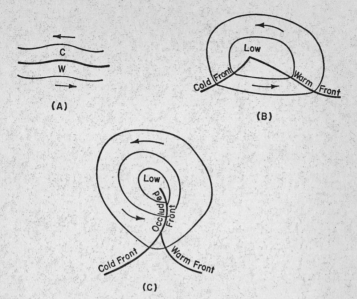

FIG. 7-1 Development of a front: (A) a wave in the westerlies, (B) breaking wave and circulation, (C) occluding of the frontal system.

pletely or mixed together, the vortex loses its intensity, and eventually dies out.

Until the region of low pressure begins to take shape, frontal systems normally will not give rise to extensive systems of clouds. However, as the waves intensify and the cold front begins to overtake the warm front, vertical motion tends to increase, causing clouds and precipitation to develop over large areas. Over the warm front there occurs a slow upsliding of moist air, giving rise to layered clouds, which may be hundreds of miles ahead of the storm center. As the center moves in from the west, the cloud bases move to lower altitudes, and more or less steady precipitation begins to fall. Once the warm front has passed to the eastward, warmer weather may appear if occlusion has not occurred. Later a second band of precipitation will move through as the cold front passes by. The advancing wedge of the cold front is steeper in slope, and the air in the warm sector may be unstable, intense vertical motion may occur. This can cause showers or thunderstorms to develop along the cold front. Violent squall lines resulting from this vertical flow can also be observed at times in the warm sector just ahead of and parallel to the cold front.

In the early theory of cyclone formation, it was proposed that the rotational motion appeared as a consequence of the interaction of air masses of different density near the surface on both sides of the front. More recent observations have indicated that large-scale disturbances in air flow at higher altitudes, such as the jet stream as well as perturbations near the ground, may contribute to the formation of cyclones. There are suggestions that coincidental superposition of high and low altitude disturbances are necessary to cyclone development. However, some cases have been reported in which a strong change at only one altitude appears sufficient to generate the vortex. Cyclones even have developed at times without an association with fronts.

Although the knowledge of the details of cyclogenesis remains incomplete, meteorologists have linked the production of kinetic energy in cyclonic disturbances to large-scale mechanisms of transformation through potential energy of disturbances, as discussed on pp. 93-94. The concentration of kinetic energy in cyclones stems directly from the non-equilibrium behavior of large masses of air of contrasting densities.

The release of energy by condensation of water vapor during ascent of moist air in cyclones is favorable to development of the vortex. However, this source of energy seems to be of secondary importance for the formation of most extratropical cyclones.

TROPICAL CYCLONES

The large, relatively persistent cyclones observed in tropical regions from 5-15° latitude are called hurricanes and typhoons. Unlike the extratropical cyclones which form in baroclinic regions, the tropical storms develop in nearly barotropic parts of the atmosphere near the equator. Hence frontal perturbations associated with a baroclinic structure in the air have little to do with the generation of the tropical cyclones.

Through the use of aircraft combined with stations on the ground, the nature of air flow in and near hurricanes is comparatively well known. The distribution of tangential velocity in these storms has nearly symmetrical character about the center of low pressure. The central core or the *eye* of the storm, about 20 km in diameter, is characterized by light winds and nearly clear skies. Interestingly enough, cyclones formed in the mid-latitudes have no observable core similar to the hurricane's eye. In the outer part of the hurricane, extending perhaps to 300 km, the spinning motion is accompanied by very strong winds varying from 35 to 70 meter sec^{-1} ($\sim$ 70-150 mph). The outer region displays towering cumulus clouds from which large amounts of precipitation fall. The cumulus clouds normally become arranged in bands spiralling like a pinwheel around the eye of the hurricane as shown in Plate V. Observations of the average distribution of radial velocity in the air indicates that a convergence near the surface exists in these storms while divergence occurs at higher altitudes. Though some anticyclonic circulation has been found near the top of hurricane vortices, the predominant circulation in these storms is cyclonic, suggesting the importance of the Coriolis force in development.

Based on the observations of tropical cyclones, a mature storm is pictured as a giant, nearly symmetrical vortex having a funnel-shaped eye oriented vertically. The boundary of the funnel spreads out and becomes diffuse near the tropical tropopause, which itself is ill-defined in this region of latitude. Radial temperature distributions suggest that there exists a gradual increase in temperature inwards towards the boundary of the funnel, but there is a jump to high temperatures inside the eye. There are indications that warm moist air tends to ascend along the outer edges of the eye while warm dry air subsides into the eye from above. Subsidence stops in the core at a stable inversion layer at altitudes of about 500-1000 meters above the surface.

Hurricanes and the Cyclostrophic Wind. Since the hurricane vortex is nearly symmetrical, the tangential motion in these storms should behave in a manner qualitatively similar to that predicted for cyclostrophic motion, a flow in concentric circles (p. 63). To explore this idea further, suppose gravity and the Coriolis acceleration are disregarded for the mature hurricane, and the flow is considered steady and barotropic. Then in the direction r, normal to streamlines,

$$\frac{\partial p}{\partial r} = \frac{\rho q^2}{r} = \rho \Omega^2 r, \qquad (7.1)$$

or

$$p = \int \frac{\rho q^2}{r} \, dr + \text{const.},$$

from Eq. (4.16). In this relation q is the tangential velocity in the horizontal plane, and Ω is the rate of rotation of the vortex. In the vortex, circulation conceivably might proceed within two limits: by rigid body rotation where $q = \Omega r$, or by motion without rotation. The second case may seem paradoxical, but we can demonstrate that fluids can flow in concentric circles without net rotation by considering the vorticity relation given by Eq. (4.4). If $(\partial u/\partial y) = (\partial v/\partial x)$, then R_{xy} equals zero, and no rotation exists in the fluid.

Under conditions of rigid body rotation, Eq. (7.1) in integrated form yields

$$p = \frac{\rho \Omega^2 r^2}{2} + \text{const.}$$

If the pressure at $r = 0$ is p_0, then

(*rigid body rotation*) $$p - p_0 = \frac{\rho \Omega^2 r^2}{2}. \qquad (7.2)$$

However, irrotational flow requires that $(\partial u/\partial y) = (\partial v/\partial x)$, or

$$\frac{\partial q}{\partial r} = -\frac{q}{r} \qquad (7.3)$$

for motion in concentric circles. Equation (7.3) yields after integration

(*irrotational motion*) $$q = \frac{B}{r}, \qquad (7.4)$$

where B is a constant. Substitution of Eq. (7.4) into Eq. (7.1) gives an expression for the pressure in terms of r:

$$p = \frac{\rho B^2}{2r^2} + \text{const.} \qquad (7.5)$$

In this kind of a limiting flow, the pressure approaches minus infinity as the radius r is reduced to zero. Hence, in evaluating the constant in Eq. (7.5) we assume that $p \rightarrow$ constant, equal to p_∞, as r approaches infinity. Then, from Eq. (7.5),

$$\text{(irrotational motion)} \qquad p_\infty - p = \frac{\rho B^2}{2r^2}. \qquad (7.6)$$

The distributions of pressure and velocity for the two limiting classes of circular flow are sketched in Fig. 7-2. For rigid body

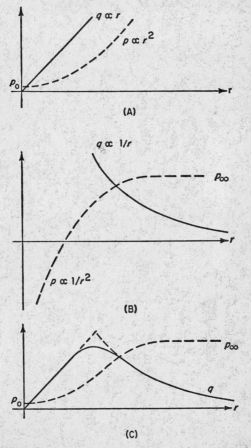

(A)

(B)

(C)

FIG. 7-2 Pressure and velocity for flow in concentric circles: (A) rigid body rotation, (B) irrotational motion, and (C) a combination of models—an ideal vortex.

rotation in Fig. 7-2(A), the tangential velocity varies linearly with r, and the pressure increases parabolically with r beginning at p_0. In Fig. 7-2(B), the case of irrotational motion is shown. The hyperbolic curve denotes the variation with r of the tangential velocity, and the pressure distribution corresponds to the curve extending from $-\infty$ to a constant value p.

In a real vortex like a hurricane, the tangential velocity increases with decreasing r in the outer portions of the storm. As the radius continues to decrease, the tangential velocity eventually reaches a maximum, then begins to decrease to approach zero at the core of the storm. Thus an idealized model of a hurricane might look like a combination of the two limiting circular flows. When the cases of rigid body rotation and irrotational flow are fitted together, the distribution of pressure and velocity in the model vortex take the form given in Fig. 7-2(C). Now a maximum in tangential velocity appears roughly at the location where the pressure changes with r most rapidly.

Qualitatively, the curves for the tangential velocity and the barometric pressure observed in hurricanes fit the picture of the ideal vortex in Fig. 7-2(C). However, in the outer portions of these storms, the tangential velocity tends to vary inversely with the square root of the radial distance rather than the first power predicted by Eq. (7.4).

It has been found that ideal vortices tend to be aerodynamically stable if the tangential flow decreases more slowly than r^{-1}. By this criterion, hurricanes can stabilize themselves for periods of a week or so by approaching a distribution of $q \propto r^{-\frac{1}{2}}$ rather than r^{-1}.

The photos in Plate V indicate that air particles in hurricanes do not move in concentric circles as assumed in the ideal model. There is instead a spin inwards near the surface with the convergence towards the center of low pressure. Thus the simple model of the ideal two-dimensional vortex in Fig. 7-2(C) cannot describe fully the hurricane.

The Origins and Maturing of Hurricanes. The detailed mechanisms for the generation and maintenance of hurricanes is still uncertain. It is known, however, that much of the energy has to come from the latent heat of vaporization of water. To release sufficient amounts of heat, strong organized motion in the vertical direction must be required to lift large masses of moist air so that extensive clouds can form. The combination of the ocean temperature reaching maximum values above about 27°C, and a peculiar configuration of winds seems to be necessary to develop and maintain the vertical motion.

Because the storms do not appear in latitudes less than 5°, the Coriolis force is believed to be important for maintaining the air in the circular paths of flow.

Considering these facts, Prof. H. Riehl and others proposed in the 1950s an explanation for hurricane formation. To start the organized vertical motion, Riehl suggested that a diverging flow at high altitudes and a converging flow at low altitudes arrive simultaneously over a point on the warm ocean. The two disturbances are associated with wave-like perturbations in the patterns of trade winds over the tropics. As the air converges, it rises because the earth's surface blocks descent. Local warming is produced initially by air masses ascending under moist adiabatic conditions from below the cloud layers to levels high in the troposphere. The release of latent heat during the ascent increases the buoyancy of the air, producing an acceleration upwards. In addition to the release of latent heat, the relatively high temperature of the air can be maintained by conduction of heat from the surface of the ocean to the air, and descent of warm dry air into the eye. As the warm moist air flows upwards along the outer boundary of the eye towards the tropopause, the diverging winds carry the rising air away from the core of the vortex. The vertical circulation is completed when the outward flowing air slowly descends to the surface far away from the center of the storm. If the temperature of the rising air remains higher than the surroundings, vertical flow will increase, causing continued decrease in pressure inside the column. To replace the rising air around the inner part of the storm, air must drift inwards. As the air whirls around in towards the core, it will rotate faster and faster until it reaches the outer boundary of the eye. The converging flow then moves upwards to the region of divergence. Inside the eye there is a decrease in tangential velocity which corresponds to rigid body rotation.

As long as the energy supplied by the sources of heat exceeds the dissipative effects such as friction, the hurricane vortex will continue to intensify. The destruction of hurricanes begins when the energy input falls below the amount necessary to maintain the motion. This usually happens when the storm moves inland. The removal of the source for warm moist air decreases the rate of introduction of energy to the vortex, and the added friction over the land increases the rate of dissipation of energy in the storm.

The strong winds generated in hurricanes and their Far East relatives, typhoons, combined with their tendency to induce the formation of very large ocean waves, and leave vast amounts of precipitation, make the tropical cyclones potentially more destructive than their larger mid-latitude cousins. Nearly every year millions of dollars in damage is caused by hurricanes as they sweep inland through the southeastern United States from the Gulf of Mexico of the Caribbean. Until the structure of hurricanes became known, the passage of the clear, calm eye was particularly troublesome. Having a false sense of security with the passing eye, people often have started cleaning up only to find the savage storm "returning" in a few hours.

ROTATIONAL DISTURBANCES ON A SMALL SCALE

Relatively stable, intense vortex motion often accompanies strong localized convection over horizontal distances of less than a kilometer. Vortices of this kind, such as *tornadoes,* sometimes originate over land in connection with violent thunderstorms. The tornado's seagoing counterpart, the *waterspout,* usually forms in cloudy air, but occasionally develops in clear skies. On even smaller scales of meters, tornado-like whirlwinds can form over spots of hot ground. These are often seen in semi-arid zones of the western United States, and they are called *dust devils.*

Tornadoes, waterspouts, and dust devils are unsteady flows having lifetimes measured in minutes. As in the case of the hurricane vortex, the distribution of pressure and velocity in these swirls is believed to be somewhat characteristic of the ideal vortex composed of nearly irrotational tangential flow around the edges, and rigid body rotation near the core. Like the hurricane, the smaller vortices have a common denominator of strong, buoyant, vertical motion associated with their generation and maintenance. Convergence in these eddies develops near the ground causing inflow towards the center of the vortices, and divergence appears at higher altitudes. Hence the idealized model of motion in concentric circles described in Fig. 7-2(C) again cannot be the complete picture of the small natural vortices.

Tornadoes and Waterspouts. In contrast to larger disturbances, whirlwinds like tornadoes or waterspouts can spin in either direction around a region of low pressure. These regular eddies are narrow and funnel shaped, and have diameters made visible by clouds or dust from about 100 meters to less than a kilometer. Tornadoes usually are marked by funnel-shaped clouds extending downward from existing clouds [Plate VI(A)]. Waterspouts, on the other hand [e.g., Plate VI(B)], though often associated with clouds, may occasionally appear as ascending columns of spray rising from the ocean's surface towards a clear sky. In the sense that these vortices occasionally are not directly linked to cloudy air, mechanistically they may be more closely related to dust devils. Although tornadoes and waterspouts are much too small to be seen on a weather map, the tornadoes particularly are locally very destructive because of sudden pressure descreases associated with their passage, and the appearance of high winds in them, which can exceed 180 meter sec^{-1} (400 mph). Waterspouts tend to be less vigorous in their rotation, and consequently less dangerous. Their comparatively small capability for destructiveness, of course, partly may be due to the fact that they pass primarily over uninhabited surfaces.

The pressure decrease associated with a tornado vortex can be extremely large in some cases. As an example, a pressure record of a tornado that touched down in Dyerburg, Tennessee in March 1952 is shown in Fig. 7-3. As the storm traveled through Dyerburg, the pressure decreased from about 74.9 cm of mercury to 72.4 cm of mercury in a few minutes. The center of the whirlwind presumably did not pass over the barograph. Hence the minimum pressure in this storm was probably considerably less than the value indicated in Fig. 7-3. Sudden changes in pressure like

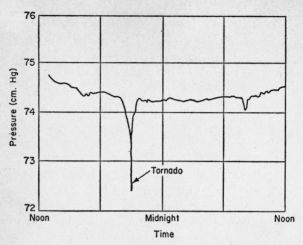

FIG. 7-3 A barograph record showing the characteristic decrease in pressure accompanying the passage of a tornado; taken when a storm passed through Dyerburg, Tennessee on March 21, 1952. [From J. A. Carr, Mon. Wea. Rev. *80*, 50-58 (1952).]

this example can cause buildings to explode because the pressure inside the structure rapidly becomes greater than the atmospheric pressure.

The appearance of a tornado is a dreaded sight. Though short lived, these vortices are so destructive that they can cut a large swath of death and disaster hundreds of meters wide right through communities. Observers have seen these storms lift up trucks and cars and set them down hundreds of meters away from their original position. Large buildings in the path of a tornado have been completely flattened. Mute testimony of the disastrous consequences of tornadoes has been especially common in American newspaper reports recently. Both 1965 and 1966 were very ravaging years for tornado activity in the midwestern and southern United States.

The Development of a Tornado. Despite the volumes of literature describing tornadoes and their effects, the exact way that nature generates and maintains these vortices remains largely unknown. Meteorologists do know that the occurrence of tornadoes accompanies very active thermal convection and thunderstorms in deep layers of excessively unstable air. Conditions for tornado formation are ripe if thick layers of dry air with a steep lapse rate (rapid temperature decrease with height) move over a moist layer near the ground. When the lower regions of the dry layer are warmer than the moist air below, an inversion develops at the boundary between the air masses. Because the inversion is hydrostatically stable, as noted in Chapter 3, this situation tends to limit small-scale convection. However, if jet-like air currents develop in the wind field aloft, a large portion of the two air layers can be lifted upwards. When this happens, both layers begin to cool with rising. But the lower moist layer will reach saturation before the upper dry air. As clouds form, the upward-moving air below will tend to cool at a moist adiabatic rate instead of the dry rate, causing an unstable situation corresponding to Case (B) in Fig. 3-5. Continued uplifting of large masses of moist air may give rise to a highly unstable condition in which near-explosive convection may develop with severe thunderstorm activity.

In zones of intense convection, a region of low pressure, called a *tornado cyclone*, may appear, which can have a diameter of 10 km or so, and with winds of about 50 mph. The tornado vortex grows inside this low-pressure zone, between its center and its right side; that is, to the right of the overall wind field, or to the right of the direction of displacement of the region of low pressure. With the intense thermal convection, vorticity becomes concentrated and vortex lines are stretched vertically in the cyclonic region. The tendency near the vortex for air to follow tangential patterns of cyclostrophic motion (p. 63) makes penetration of air along the sides of the column difficult. Thus air can enter the vortex mainly through the top and bottom. Although Helmholtz's theorem on p. 54 requires that the vortex lines in the tornado cannot end in the fluid, the existence of wind shear above and at the ground can effectively terminate the columnar vortex by frictionally diffusing the vertically oriented vortex lines laterally at the ends. As converging buoyant air enters the vortex from below, it tends to rise without mixing with environmental air because of existence of the cyclostrophic "shell" of the column. Hence the rising air particles can accelerate upwards in a highly unstable configuration. The resulting vertical motion continues to stretch the vortex lines vertically, intensifying the spinning motion by conservation of angular momentum, as described on p. 55. Furthermore, vorticity in the air below the cloud and in the boundary layer near the ground can be carried up into the vortex by the rising air to "feed" the tornado with more spinning motion. At the top, the spreading of the funnel during divergence of flow is accompanied by mixing of cold air down into the core of the vortex. The descending cool air inhibits extension of the column upwards, and the frictional effect tends to dissipate the spinning motion by diffusing of vorticity horizontally.

There have been indications that vortices like tornadoes have strong upward motion in the core, but have a downward drift at the edges of the funnel as drawn in Fig. 7-4. This kind of vertical

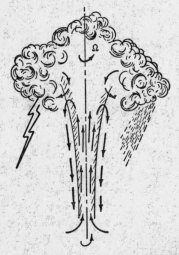

FIG. 7-4   Idealized vertical flow in a tornado vortex.

circulation would give rise to the downward extension of the visible funnel cloud of the tornado as it grows. Cloud droplets would be dragged down with the downdraft of air around the periphery of the vortex. Reduction of pressure during the concentration of spinning motion in the vortex would cause condensation of water vapor to occur in the column. Presumably this effect also would appear visually to be quite similar to the extension of the funnel by peripheral down flow.

Meteorologists sometimes have questioned whether buoyant convection concentrated in the core of a tornado can provide sufficient energy to maintain the intense circulation in these vortices. The observation that lightning flashes often take place with unusual frequency in tornado funnels has led some workers to believe that these storms may have electrodynamic origins of energy. For example, B. Vonnegut has suggested that the spinning motion initially induced in a thunderstorm can provide a stabilizing path for electrical discharge in the storm. Current flow to the ground by frequent lightning flashes through the core of the vortex could provide substantial heating to rising air in this region, giving the possibility for a larger source of energy to maintain the spinning flow than by local heating from the ground, or from condensation alone.

Vonnegut's ideas stem in part from very old notions of electrical mechanisms for weather phenomena. Some of these concepts have been described by the baroque Russian poet-meteorologist, M. V. Lomonosov in 1753, and later by the French physicist J. C. A. Peltier, one of the discoverers of the thermo-electric effect. Vonnegut has noted that electrodynamic meteorology was a very popular competitor to thermodynamic-hydrodynamic meteorology at the turn of the nineteenth century. However, curiously enough, the electrical mechanisms lost much of their appeal by the middle 1800s because of the vigorous work of the thermodynamicists and hydrodynamicists, who gave many simple and plausible explanations for atmospheric behavior.

Because of the special conditions that seem necessary for tornado generation, certain locations are especially susceptible to this kind of storm. Regions near the Mississippi Valley are perhaps the greatest spawning places of tornadoes in the world. The high-altitude source of warm dry air traveling from the Pacific coast to the east and the moist air surging northward from the Gulf of Mexico, give the potential for development of massive penetrative convection. And, at the same time, the existence of strong westerlies above with southerly flow of air below provides the wind shear for massive disturbances of the two air layers. The probability of these events assembling together reaches a maximum in North America by the late spring. This is the time of the year when tornadoes are most frequently observed in the middle United States.

Dust Devils. Much less devastating, but just as interesting are the tiny tornado-like whirlwinds originating from severe localized heating at the surface of the earth. These regular vortices range in size from a few meters to about 20 meters in diameter. They last for a few seconds to a minute or so, and rarely extend more than approximately 1500 meters in altitude. Like tornadoes and waterspouts, dust devils can rotate in either direction depending on their origin. To generate a dust devil, hot air near the ground must gain an organized spin in the horizontal plane. This can occur, for example, from eddies shedding away from isolated hills or trees as air flows around these obstacles. The hot spinning air in these eddies tends to concentrate into a vertically oriented columnar vortex with air rising in its core. In moving towards a structure like cyclostrophic flow, air particles will spin tangentially around the column and help to prevent air from penetrating the sides of the vortex. Hence the energy is fed to the vortex via exchange of potential energy to kinetic energy via buoyant air entering the bottom of the vortex as it moves over the hot ground with a light wind. As the hot air ascends inside the column, the vortex lines stretch, and vorticity introduced at the ground is intensified. Eventually the rising warm air in the dust devil begins to mix with cooler, nonrotating air near the top of the column. The cooler air tends to descend through the top, which, accompanied by a divergence of air outwards into the surroundings, spreads out the rotating core. The outward flow can be traced visibly by particles of dust that spin away from the top of the column.

Dust devils may extend upwards several times during their brief lives. But as the buoyant, rotating air mixes with its surroundings, rotation is lost, the whirlwind meets its demise, and its top retreats to the ground.

Laboratory Analysis of Vortex Flow. The mechanisms of flow in tornado-like vortices have eluded scientists for a long time. Hope for finding answers to the puzzles of these eddies has sent some workers into the laboratory to study hydrodynamic analogies like those of the thermally driven circulations discussed in Chapter 6. One of the earliest attempts to reproduce tornadoes in the laboratory was reported by J. C. Wilcke in 1780. This experimenter formed vortices in tanks of water by spinning a paddle wheel in the liquid. More recently, some studies of tornado-like disturbances in air by C. C. Chang of Catholic University have had certain popular appeal. Other demonstrations of concentrated vortices induced by buoyant motion have been given by J. S. Turner of Woods Hole Oceanographic Institution and D. K. Lilly of the National Center for Atmospheric Research. In one of their experiments, vortices were generated in a long cylinder filled with water. The cylinder was rotated on a turntable until steady rotational motion developed in the water. Changes in density were introduced by bubbling air into the upper layers of water along the axis of rotation. The bubbling induced a vertical component of flow in the fluid near its axis of rotation. A vortex then developed which was concentrated near the center of the cylinder.

A typical vortex in laminar flow is shown in Plate XI. This has a striking resemblance to the natural vortices in Plate VI. The vertical structure of flow was traced by adding dye to the water. Potassium permanganate crystals were introduced at the bottom and India ink was injected at the top of the tank. Observations of the dispersion of ink and dye showed that there was strong upward flow in the core of the vortex, combined with a weaker downward drift along the outer edges of the vortex, thus strengthening the proposed pattern of vertical circulation in tornadoes (Fig. 7-4). As shown in Plate XI(B), the two regions of flow appeared as thin cylindrical sheets of ink moving downward around the thread-like, upward-moving core of permanganate dye.

8 *Eddies—Turbulence*

CHARACTERIZING TURBULENT FLOW

Superimposed on the patterns of average motion in the atmosphere are the small fluctuations. If one measures a component of velocity with an anemometer having reasonably rapid response to wind changes, the turbulent oscillations in the wind readily can be recorded. As an example, a record of a signal from a hot wire anemometer described in Chapter 2 is shown in Fig. 8-1. Here.

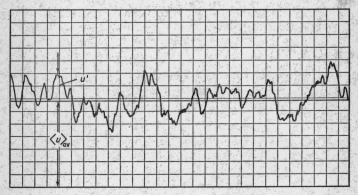

FIG. 8-1 A time record of wind variation from a hot wire anemometer.

the variation in time of the wind shows perturbations of a statistically random nature fluctuating about an average value $\langle u \rangle_{av}$, which is assumed invariant over long periods of time. The oscillations in air speed recorded by such a fixed instrument are identified with weak eddies traveling with the wind past the anemometer. Thus, turbulent flow generally is characterized by its secondary, non-steady, random or disordered rotational component superimposed on the mean motion. In other words, turbulence can be defined as a random field of vorticity traveling with the wind (see also p. 128). The randomness in rotation implies that the local velocity of the fluid at any point in space varies in an unordered way which is roughly analogous to the chaotic thermal agitation of molecules in a gas.

Dispersive Power. A striking feature of turbulence is observed whenever traces of contaminant are introduced into the moving fluid. The irregular rotational motion causes the localized spots of matter to be mixed more uniformly throughout the entire volume of fluid. Similarly, localized regions of high temperature will be smoothed out by the eddying motion. If two neighboring particles are marked in a field of turbulent flow, they will always tend to move away from each other. Each particle may follow a tortuous path, but, on the average, they will be found farther and farther apart. The property of dispersing anything possessed by the fluid particles in eddying motion serves as another definition of turbulence.

The dispersion of contaminants by turbulence is illustrated in the photograph of the cigarette smoke in Plate VII(A). As the air begins to move, the suspended particles of smoke rise in a tube which corresponds to laminar flow. The smoke particles follow the distortion of fluid elements as they begin to rotate and stretch. Filaments or strings of fluid are twisted into curves. By intertwining and convoluting of the filaments, the fluid as traced by the smoke particles becomes mixed rapidly into the surrounding air.

On a little larger scale, a familiar example of the diffusive power of a turbulent wind is shown in the smoke plume of Plate VII(B). Particles of smoke are observed to disperse quickly into the environment as they are blown away from the stack.

The Generation of Turbulence. Turbulent motion in a fluid can result from the effects of shearing motion, or from the influences of unstable stratification in density.[1] In Chapter 6 we dis-

[1] The large scale patterns of eddying in atmospheric currents also are non-steady and irregular over long periods of time as discussed in Chapter

cussed briefly that the onset of turbulence in shearing flows depends on the magnitude of the inertial forces as compared with the viscous forces. Instability in shearing layers leading to the formation of vortices was also discussed in connection with velocity discontinuities such as the one in Fig. 4-11. The S-shaped velocity profile associated with regions of shear in fluids marks particularly an unstable configuration of flow. The transition from laminar motion to turbulent motion in a fluid is reflected in the Reynolds number characteristic of the flow (p. 119).

Turbulence that is generated purely by the effects of friction can occur only in cases where the fluid is homogeneous in density, or under conditions where the fluid is stable; i.e., from the criterion on p. 121, $S \geqslant 0$. When the stability parameter S is less than zero, the formation of turbulence will also depend on overturning by buoyant convection. Approximate homogeneity in density may develop in the atmosphere near the ground where skies are heavily overcast. If the sky is clear over level ground, substantial differences in the stratification of air may be observed during periods of 24 hours. For example, during the night, there is no solar heating and energy must radiate away from the earth's surface. This can cause layers of air near the surface to cool and become denser than warmer air above, and this can lead in turn to a hydrostatically stable environment. When the sun rises, the ground will begin to be heated, giving rise to warming of air near the surface, and a consequent development of unstable conditions in stratification. The energy supplied to maintain turbulence comes largely from the average air motion. Thus in the absence of shearing flow, turbulence must inevitably die down at night because the average air motion tends to be reduced, and consequently no sources of energy will exist away from the surface under these conditions $(S \geqslant 0)$. However, the heating by the sun's radiation during the day can produce circumstances where overturning motion increases, and more energy becomes available to maintain turbulent motion. The onset of strong penetrative

---

5. Hence, these vortices are sometimes considered statistically on a time scale of years as turbulence. As discussed in Chapter 7, the larger eddies are related to baroclinic instabilities involving horizontal contrasts in density as well as to instabilities in the vertical structure of the atmosphere.

convection and turbulence during the day often is reflected in the familiar sight of the development of thunderstorms by late morning or early afternoon during the summer months.

The energy related to turbulence existing in stably stratified air often can be completely consumed in doing work against gravity. If turbulence persists in a nominally stable environment, there must, of course, be a source of energy for the motion. There are two sources of energy which can contribute to developing turbulence away from boundaries. The first source comes from localized instabilities where $S < 0$. Such situations may develop over hot spots on the earth's surface like a city (see also p. 114). The second depends, of course, on the existence of shear in the fluid. The connection between density gradients and shearing flow in generating and sustaining turbulent motion was demonstrated many years ago by the German aerodynamicist, L. Prandtl, and the English scientist, L. Richardson. A criterion for stability in stratified media based on the ideas of Richardson will be discussed later in connection with Eq. (8.6).

Portraying the Properties of Turbulent Flow. Because turbulent motion changes in space and time in a random way, the detailed structure of the properties of the flow field at any instant is exceedingly difficult to specify, and has relatively little practical interest. Attention then is centered on the properties of the motion which have been averaged in different ways. Frequently, the easiest way to treat experimental data is to consider averaging at a point in space over a period of time.

To facilitate statistical analysis, measurable properties of the fluid such as the velocity, the pressure, or the temperature are defined as in the case of large-scale motion, p. 91, in such a way that the instantaneous value consists of the sum of an average component and a fluctuating term. That is,

$$\mathbf{U}(\mathbf{x},t) = \langle \mathbf{u}(\mathbf{x}) \rangle_{av} + \mathbf{u}'(\mathbf{x},t). \tag{8.1}$$

Hence, relations like Eq. (5.3) serve to define the average and the fluctuating component of velocity, $\langle \mathbf{u} \rangle_{av}$ and $\mathbf{u}'$. These terms also are illustrated graphically for the signal in Fig. 8-1.

Definitions of properties of a field of turbulent flow like Eq. (5.3) or Eq. (8.1) work satisfactorily for studying fluid motion where the properties are independent of the assumed time interval for averaging. Unfortunately, it has not been possible to determine completely the criterion for the average and fluctuating parts of fluid properties in geophysical problems. Wind speeds, for example, vary at the same place over a wide range from centimeters per minute to meters per year. The question of taking meaningful averages in such cases has not been satisfactorily resolved. In spite of this difficulty, it is assumed that, for practical purposes, relations such as Eq. (8.1) provide a useful framework for studying at least the microscale motion in the atmosphere.

Two quantities frequently are used for comparing various configurations of turbulent flow. These are the *intensity* and the *scale*. The intensity $[\langle u'^2 \rangle_{av}/\langle u \rangle^2_{av}]^{1/2}$ measures the strength of a turbulent disturbance relative to the strength of the average wind. Intensities are normally much less than one, as must be assumed for the use of Eq. (8.1). The scale refers to a measure of the *extent of correlation* between local velocities at two different points in space or in time. Complete correlation means that the velocity at point 1 is the same as the velocity at point 2. No correlation means that the velocities have no relation to each other at the two different points. Physically, the scale taken spatially is often interpreted as a kind of weighted average size of eddies in a turbulent system.

The length scale also serves as a characteristic parameter for turbulent mixing or dispersion. The length scale can only become as finely grained as the size of the smallest eddies, which cannot reach sizes below about 0.1 cm diameter in air. Eddies of this size still contain a multitude of molecules so that further mixing must result from the processes of molecular diffusion.

To find the relation between the fluctuations and the mean properties of the fluid, Eq. (8.1) is substituted with similar relations for pressure and density into the equation of motion, Eq. (4.22), and an average is taken with respect to time at each point in the fluid volume. The resulting expression contains a relation among the average velocity, the average gradient in pressure, the frictional force in terms of the viscosity and the gradient of the average velocity, the covariances of density fluctuation ρ', and the components of the fluctuating velocity vector u', v', and w'. For a fluid of constant density, the covariances have forms such as $\rho\langle u'u'\rangle_{av}$, or $\rho\langle u'v'\rangle_{av}$, where u' is the fluctuating velocity in the (horizontal) x direction and w' is the component of fluctuating velocity in the vertical direction, z. These numbers have the units of force per unit area (stress) or of viscosity times a gradient in velocity. They represent an average rate of transfer of momentum by the movement of eddies from one region of space to another (see also p. 91). For example, the term $\rho\langle u'w'\rangle_{av}$ is the average rate of horizontal momentum transferred vertically by the eddy motion. The analogy between the viscous stresses and the covariance in velocity was first used by Sir Osborne Reynolds in 1895. Therefore, the terms such as $\rho\langle u'w'\rangle_{av}$ are called the *Reynolds stresses,* in honor of their discoverer.

THE AVERAGE SHEAR AND THE REYNOLDS STRESS

The equation for average motion in a turbulent medium can be put into the same form as Eq. (4.16) if an average stress $\langle\tau\rangle_{av}$ is defined such that the Reynolds stresses are assumed to be proportional to the mean shear. For the component $\langle\tau_{zx}\rangle_{av}$:

$$\langle\tau_{zx}\rangle_{av} = (\mu + \rho\mathcal{E}_\nu)\frac{\partial\langle u\rangle_{av}}{\partial z} \tag{8.2}$$

where μ is the molecular viscosity, and $\mathcal{E}_\nu$ is the eddy viscosity or the transfer coefficient for momentum. In effect, Eq. (8.2) defines the relation between the eddy viscosity and the Reynolds stress:

$$\mathcal{E}_\nu = \frac{\rho\langle u'w'\rangle_{av}}{(\partial\langle u\rangle_{av}/\partial z)}. \tag{8.3}$$

The molecular viscosity is a physical property of the fluid while $\mathcal{E}_\nu$ depends on the turbulence, and hence it may vary in both time and in space with the motion. The eddy viscosity ordinarily has been found to be very much larger than the molecular viscosity.

Mixing Length Theory. For practical calculations of the distribution of average velocity in turbulent shear flows, one must know how $\mathcal{E}_\nu$ changes with the motion. A classical theory which relates the eddy viscosity to the velocity is the mixing length hypotheses of L. Prandtl in 1925, and G. I. Taylor in 1932 Prandtl assumed that the transfer of momentum by turbulent motion was analogous to transfer by molecular agitation in gases. A result from the kinetic theory of gases indicates that the viscosity is proportional to a characteristic length and a characteristic speed. As an analogy, Prandtl assumed on dimensional grounds that the eddy viscosity in a statistically steady system of turbulence in the z direction takes the form:

$$\mathcal{E}_\nu = \langle u'^2 \rangle_{\rm av}^{1/2} \mathcal{L}, \tag{8.4}$$

where $\mathcal{L}$ denotes a mixing length, which depends on position in space. Prandtl reasoned that the velocity with which fluid particles move vertically across a horizontal fluid layer must be the order of:

$$\langle u'^2 \rangle_{\rm av}^{1/2} \sim \pm (\partial \langle u \rangle_{\rm av} / \partial z).$$

Therefore, the contribution of turbulence to the average shear stress given by Eq. (8.2) must be proportional to the absolute value of the average velocity gradient. If the molecular viscosity is much smaller than the eddy viscosity,

$$\langle \tau_{zx} \rangle_{\rm av} \approx \rho \langle u'w' \rangle_{\rm av} = \rho \mathcal{L}^2 \left| \frac{\partial \langle u \rangle_{\rm av}}{\partial z} \right| \left(\frac{\partial \langle u \rangle_{\rm av}}{\partial z} \right). \tag{8.5}$$

Taylor found in 1932 a result similar to Eq. (8.5), but he assumed that vorticity rather than momentum was the transportable quantity.

Experimental measurements of the average velocity in different kinds of shear flows have been compared with predictions from the two mixing length theories. For practical purposes, there is reasonably good agreement between the observations and the analytical results of either theory when the arbitrary length scale $\mathcal{L}$ is estimated from the experimental data.

The Reynolds Stresses and Stability. Mixing length theory supplies a method for relating the velocity fluctuations of turbulent flow to hydrostatic stability in stratified fluids. To illustrate this, let us consider what happens to an element of non-homogeneous fluid in a turbulent shearing flow. If the fluid is stably stratified, vertical mixing must eventually be destroyed at distances far from the surface. The location where turbulence disappears in a stably stratified medium then will depend to a great extent on the magnitude of the horizontal velocity increase with height (the shear). From Eqs. (8.3) and (8.4), the order of magnitude of the vertical velocity fluctuations in the fluid are given by

$$w' \sim \mathcal{L}\frac{\partial \langle u \rangle_{\mathrm{av}}}{\partial z}.$$

The kinetic energy of an element of unit volume in vertical motion accordingly is

$$\tfrac{1}{2}\langle \rho \rangle_{\mathrm{av}} w'^2 = \tfrac{1}{2}\langle \rho \rangle_{\mathrm{av}}\mathcal{L}^2\left(\frac{\partial \langle u \rangle_{\mathrm{av}}}{\partial z}\right)^2.$$

If the fluid is incompressible, the work done in lifting the element from an equilibrium position at z_0 to a layer at z_1, W, is calculated from the buoyancy force per unit volume F, namely,

$$F = g(\rho_0 - \rho_1) = g\frac{d\rho}{dz}(z_0 - z_1),$$

and

$$W = \int_{z_0} F\,dz = \int_{z_0}^{z_0+\mathcal{L}} F\,dz = -\tfrac{1}{2}g\mathcal{L}^2\frac{d\rho}{dz}.$$

In the upper limit, where existing turbulence will be suppressed instead of growing in intensity, the kinetic energy of the element has to equal the work done in raising the element, or

$$-g\frac{d\rho}{dz} = \langle \rho \rangle_{\mathrm{av}}\left(\frac{\partial \langle u \rangle_{\mathrm{av}}}{\partial z}\right)^2. \tag{8.6}$$

The ratio of the left side and the right side of Eq. (8.6) is named the Richardson number, Ri, in honor of L. Richardson. From Eq. (3.6) giving the relation between the density gradient and the stability parameters, we note that

$$Ri = \frac{gS}{\langle \rho \rangle_{\mathrm{av}}\left(\dfrac{\partial \langle u \rangle_{\mathrm{av}}}{\partial z}\right)^2}. \tag{8.7}$$

In cases where the fluid is homogeneous in density, $Ri = 0$. If $Ri > 0$, conditions are stably layered, and when $Ri < 0$, the fluid is unstably stratified. Workers have found that the motion in stratified fluids will not become turbulent if $Ri \geqslant 0.25$, provided that the velocity gradient is linear. In the case of laminar boundary layers, the flow in the layer will tend to remain stable if $Ri \geqslant 0.042$.

The balance in Eq. (8.6) indicates that even turbulence generated by shearing flow can die away in the presence of stable gradients in density. Thus vertical motion in surface layers of air during the day can be destroyed even in the presence of winds as layers of the air become more stable with cooling during the night. Since horizontal motion can be largely unaffected by increased stability, air motion during the night may tend to be confined to horizontal layers.

Vertical Distributions of Horizontal Velocity. The distribution of horizontal velocity in the vertical direction is a feature of interest in geophysical problems. The flow in the atmosphere and in the oceans is usually turbulent near a surface. An idea of the velocity distribution in the (turbulent) boundary layer can be obtained by applying the results of the mixing length theory.

To deduce a relation for the average wind profile, let us apply Eq. (8.5) to the case of air flow under neutral conditions. If the boundary layer is thin, $\langle \tau_{zx} \rangle_{av}$ and ρ are nearly constant. Therefore, the friction velocity $u^* = (\tau_{zx}/\rho)^{1/2}$ is also approximately constant. We expect that the mixing length depends on the size of the eddies which are being generated. So, as an approximation, the mixing length is assumed to be proportional to the vertical distance from the ground, of $\mathcal{L} = \kappa z$, where κ is called Karman's constant. Experimental observations have shown that κ has a value of about 0.4. If Karman's constant is substituted into Eq. (8.5), the velocity gradient is

$$\frac{\partial \langle u \rangle_{av}}{\partial z} = \frac{u^*}{\kappa z}. \tag{8.8}$$

Integration of (8.8) with respect to z, assuming u^* remains constant, gives:

$$\langle u \rangle_{av} = \frac{u^*}{\kappa} \ln z + \text{const.}$$

Because the fluid velocity is always zero along a solid boundary, there must be a region near the surface where the viscosity controls the frictional force. This region, called the *viscous sublayer*, is normally very thin, and it lies between the surface and the turbulent boundary layer. To account for the motion in the sublayer, the velocity in Eq. (8.8) is arranged to approach u_0 at an arbitrary height z_0. Therefore, Eq. (8.8) in integrated form becomes

$$\langle u \rangle_{av} - u_0 = \frac{u^*}{\kappa} \ln (z/z_0). \qquad (8.9)$$

Equation (8.9) is the well known relation for the *logarithmic wind profile*. The symbol z_0 is called the *roughness parameter*. It depends on the irregularities on the ground. Roughness can include grass, trees, rocks, houses, etc. Values of z_0 can vary from a fraction of a millimeter to several meters depending on the kind of irregularity on the surface.

The ocean's surface develops a naturally varying roughness induced by the wind—waves. Values of z_0 for the water surface change with the height and shape of the waves, which simultaneously depend on the wind speed. The variation in the roughness of the oceans is an important factor in determining the transfer of moisture and energy from the ocean to the atmosphere. The exchange of energy between the oceans and the atmosphere is an interesting example of feed-back in natural processes. We know that much of the sun's energy goes into the atmosphere through the intermediary of the oceans. The atmosphere returns some of the energy to the surface of the sea via the winds. The details of the mechanism for energy transfer across the air-water boundary are still not clear. This problem remains one of the important unsolved problems in fluid mechanics.

Wind Profiles under Non-Neutral Conditions. When the atmosphere exists in conditions of stratification which are not neutral, the logarithmic profile, Eq. (8.9), does not describe adequately the wind observations. To account for the influence of conditions of stability, the Russian scientists A. S. Monin and A. M. Obukhov have proposed a modification of the classical theory based on the mixing length. They have suggested that flow in the atmospheric surface layer depends only on three basic parameters, u^*, z_0, and another characteristic length L. These parameters are assumed independent of height, z. The characteristic length L is related to Richardson number in the following way:

$$L \approx \frac{u^*}{\kappa Ri} \left(\frac{\partial \langle u \rangle_{\mathrm{av}}}{\partial z} \right)^{-1}, \tag{8.10}$$

provided that the eddy coefficient for heat transfer is the same as the eddy coefficient for momentum transfer.

For the case where the atmosphere exhibits small departures from neutral stability, Monin and Obukhov write the Prandtl relation, Eq. (8.8), as

$$\frac{\partial \langle u \rangle_{\mathrm{av}}}{\partial z} = \frac{u^*}{\kappa z} \left[1 + \frac{\beta z}{L} \right], \tag{8.11}$$

where β is a constant, found by experiment to be approximately five. Integrating (8.11), we find that

$$\langle u \rangle_{\mathrm{av}} - u_0 \cong \frac{u^*}{\kappa} \left[\ln \frac{z}{z_0} + \frac{\beta z}{L} \right], \tag{8.12}$$

neglecting the term $\beta z_0 / L$, which is ordinarly quite small for atmospheric conditions. This relation corresponds to the logarithmic wind profile [Eq. (8.9)] with a first-order correction for the influence of hydrostatic stability of the air near the surface.

Equation (8.12) seems to work remarkably well for correlating observations of wind profiles near the ground for a relatively wide range of Richardson number.

The Distribution of Kinetic Energy in Turbulent Flow. In turbulent flow, eddies have a wide variety of size, orientation, and strength of rotation. Each of these properties is related statistically to the mean flow and the distance from the source of turbulence to the location of observation. To characterize turbulence in air, it often is necessary to examine the distribution of kinetic energy in various modes of the air motion in addition to considering the intensity and scale of turbulence. One useful way of looking at the kinetic energy of eddies centers attention on the apportioning according to size of the eddies, ℓ. It is customary to consider a spectral distribution of energy spread over ranges of reciprocal size, $k \sim \ell^{-1}$. The energy contained in $(k + dk)$ sized eddies corresponds to a value of $e(k)dk$, where dk is a differential element of the reciprocal length k. If we plot $e(k)$ vs. k

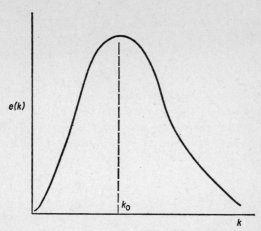

FIG. 8-2 The spectrum of kinetic energy in a turbulent medium.

for a representative field of turbulence, a distribution curve like the one in Fig. 8-2 is obtained. The total kinetic energy E per unit mass of fluid is the sum of all the components $e(k)dk$ of the distribution, or:

$$E = \int_0^\infty e(k) \, dk \qquad (8.13)$$

where $e(k)$ has the dimension of $[L^3T^{-2}]$. The right side of Eq. (8.13) represents the area under the curve in Fig. 8-2. There is a scale k_0 of the turbulent motion where most of the energy is concentrated. In the larger eddies, the energy decreases to zero because of their inertia. Energy also decreases in the smallest eddies because of the dissipative effects of viscosity, discussed on p. 68.

The idea of an energy spectrum also has application to the study of the distribution of kinetic energy with orientation of eddies. To determine the classification of energy by size and orientation of eddies, we could rewrite Eq. (8.13) in terms of vector reciprocal length, $\mathbf{k}$. Then the specification of the total energy E would require an integration similar to Eq. (8.13) for all three components of the vector wave number, $\mathbf{k}$.

To get an idea of the mechanism for distribution of kinetic energy between eddies, let us look at a homogeneous fluid which contains a variety of eddies. Without the effect of viscosity, the vorticity, which is proportional to angular velocity, remains with the individual particles of ideal fluid (see also Chapter 4). As particles become farther apart, on the average, the vortex lines tend to be stretched. The size of eddies decreases with the stretching. If the angular momentum is conserved, the distortion causes the vorticity to increase. Simultaneously the kinetic energy must tend to increase since it depends on the square of the angular velocity. The additional action of viscosity tends to remove the energy from the fluid particles. The dissipation resulting from viscosity depends on the shear, which in turn is proportional to the vorticity. As the vorticity increases in the smaller eddies, the viscous dissipation also increases. The loss of energy by friction works on eddies of all sizes, but its effect is most strongly felt in the smallest scale motion where the local gradients in velocity are greatest. Hence, a smooth distribution of energy over all sizes takes a shape which exhibits a maximum somewhere in the middle size range as sketched in Fig. 8-2.

What happens to the distribution of energy as eddies diffuse away from a source such as a rough boundary? Initially we would expect that the maximum size of eddies should correspond to a characteristic size of the original disturbance. For example, eddies shedding away from ground roughened by bushes or a house, as in Fig. 6-7, should have a size of the same order as the heights of these obstacles. As an element of turbulent fluid moves downstream from the source, the distribution of energy among the eddies changes. In the absence of other sources of energy, the total energy contained in the fluid represented by the area under the curve in Fig. 8-2 gradually decreases. In addition, the energy is transferred from the larger to the smaller eddies while the viscous effects remove energy principally from the smaller sizes. Since the rate of transfer of energy to smaller eddies is generally less than the rate of dissipation by viscosity, the finer scale eddies tend to decay more rapidly than they are produced as the eddies move downstream. Therefore, the average size of remaining eddies tends to increase. Eventually all that remains in the final stages of decay are the very large, slowly rotating eddies, which, in turn, ultimately die out.

Kolmogoroff's Theory. Under some circumstances the distribution of energy in the range of small eddies tends to approach a steady state or an equilibrium distribution. It is believed that the process of distribution energy in the range of smaller eddies becomes internally self-adjusting through the action of inertial forces and friction. It is assumed that, in the equilibrium range, the introduction and dissipation of energy proceed at a constant rate ϵ, and the removal of energy depends only on the kinematic viscosity of the fluid, v.

A simple theory for predicting the shape of the equilibrium range of eddies has been proposed by the Russian statistician, A. N. Kolmogoroff. His hypothesis of *universal equilibrium* requires that the motion associated with the equilibrium range is locally *isotropic*,[2] and the motion is uniquely determined statistically by the parameters ϵ and v. Once these assumptions are made, the shape of the equilibrium range can be determined by *dimensional arguments* alone. Kolmogoroff specified the equilibrium range of the energy distribution in terms of a characteristic length η and a characteristic velocity q:

$$\eta = \left(\frac{v^3}{\epsilon}\right)^{1/4}, \qquad q = (v\epsilon)^{1/2}. \tag{8.14}$$

We note that ϵ and v respectively have the dimensions of energy per unit mass lost per unit time, or in terms of length L and time T, $[L^2T^{-3}]$ and $[L^2T^{-1}]$. Using η and q, $e(k)$ for the equilibrium range is found to be:

$$e(k) = \eta q^2 \psi(\eta k) \tag{8.15}$$

where ψ is a "universal" function of the product of η and k. This result is quite important because it implies that the distribution of energy in the eddies that develop in many different ways may be similar over a certain range of (small) eddy sizes.

The Inertial Subrange. An important requirement for reaching the equilibrium range calls for the Reynolds number characteristic of the flow to be very large. This suggests that the motion associated with the eddies that contain most of the turbulent en-

[2]G. I. Taylor has defined isotropic turbulence by the condition that the average values of the flow variables, such as the velocity U or the vorticity ω, should be independent of translation, rotation, and reflection of the coordinate axes of reference.

ergy should be dominated by the inertial forces. Conditions fitting this criterion are found if the length scale of the energy containing eddies k_0 is much less than the scale k_d associated with the dissipation range. That is, in some cases there may be a subrange in the equilibrium distribution. The *inertial subrange* should be roughly independent of v. The dissipation subrange $(k_d \gg k_0)$ should be controlled principally by the frictional forces (but not independent of ϵ. For the inertial subrange, we find that:

$$\text{(Inertial subrange)} \quad e(k) = B\epsilon^{2/3}k^{-5/3}, \quad (8.16)$$

where B is an arbitrary constant.

Recently some measurements of the turbulent energy distributions for cases of geophysical interest (very high Reynolds number) have been made by R. W. Stewart and co-workers in Canada. Data were taken in ocean currents and in winds over the sea. The oceanic data were measured in the Seymour Narrows between Vancouver Island and Quadra Island. The Reynolds number based on the mean channel flow and the width of the narrows was approximately 10^8. Their measurements showed that a significant equilibrium range existed in which $e(k)$ varied as $k^{-5/3}$. The values of ϵ and B were found to be about $1.6 \cdot 10^{-3}$ cm^2 sec^{-3} and 1.4. Their measurements of the distribution of energy in winds over water gave about the same value for B, and displayed the inverse $5/3$ power variation in $e(k)$.

There is still a certain amount of disagreement among the theoreticians about the shape of the function $e(k)$ in the region where the spectrum is controlled by the frictional forces. Some of the theoretical work indicates that $e(k)$ should be proportional to k^{-7} in this range. Experiments of Stewart, *et al.* tend to verify this decrease in $e(k)$ for high values of k.

DISPERSION OF MATERIAL BY TURBULENT MOTION

The property of turbulent fields for dispersion material more uniformly through a medium has considerable practical interest to workers dealing with small-scale processes in the atmosphere.

The manner of dispersal of traces of materials like water vapor, carbon dioxide, ozone, organic vapors, dust, and smoke is quite relevant to the environment conditions in which we live. The distribution of the first three substances affect the transfer of solar energy to and from the earth. An example of the importance of the last four materials comes from air pollution problems such as the formation of smog.

The dispersion of material by turbulent agitation is closely allied to processes of diffusion involving molecular motion. The spreading of material in a fluid at rest or in laminar flow depends on the random agitation relative to the average speed of travel of the fluid body. This random motion in quiescent fluids was discovered in 1830 by the English botanist R. Brown during his microscopic studies of the behavior of pollen grains suspended in a fluid. The peculiar movement of the tiny particles was traced to impulses resulting from differences in kinetic energy transferred to the particles during collisions with surrounding molecules. At the beginning of the twentieth century, many physicists became interested in the statistical behavior of systems undergoing Brownian motion. At this time, Einstein made an important disclosure about diffusion in such systems. Einstein found that the mean square displacement of small particles, or molecules undergoing Brownian motion, is proportional to the time Δt for the particle to travel a distance X.

$$\langle X^2 \rangle_{av} = 2D\ \Delta t, \tag{8.17}$$

where half the constant of proportionality is called the diffusivity, D.

Einstein's methods of deriving Eq. (8.17) also may be applied to turbulent dispersion. To use the principles underlying the theory of Brownian motion in turbulence, it is useful to consider dispersion in terms of trajectories traced by individual elements of fluid taken in the Lagrangian frame of reference. This approach, called *diffusion by continuous movement,* was first discussed in 1921 by G. I. Taylor.

To illustrate Taylor's analysis, let us focus attention on an element of fluid moving in the x direction in a field of (isotropic) turbulent motion. The element is tagged at time t equal to zero, at location $x = a$. If the Lagrangian velocity[3] of the fluid particle is

$$v_p(a,t) = \frac{dX}{dt}, \qquad (8.18)$$

where X is the relative displacement, $x(t) - a(0)$, then

$$X(a,t) = \int_0^t v_p(a,t_1)\, dt_1. \qquad (8.19)$$

In the statistics of particle behavior, the mean square displacement, $\langle X^2 \rangle_{av}$ is of central importance. To find this property, Eqs. (8.18) and (8.19) are first multiplied together:

$$X\frac{dX}{dt} = \tfrac{1}{2}\frac{dX^2}{dt} = v_p(a,t)\int_0^t v_p(a,t_1)\, dt_1. \qquad (8.20)$$

Since $v_p(a,t)$ does not depend on the variable of integration on the right side of Eq. (8.20) it may be taken inside this integral. Averaging Eq. (8.20) for the trajectories of a very large number of particles starting at a, one finds that[4]

$$\frac{d\langle X^2 \rangle_{av}}{dt} = 2\langle v_p{}^2 \rangle_{av}\int_0^t R_L(a,t,t_1)\, dt_1, \qquad (8.21)$$

where the Lagrangian correlation coefficient

$$R_L = \frac{\langle v_p(a,t)v_p(a,t_1)\rangle_{av}}{\langle v_p{}^2 \rangle_{av}}. \qquad (8.21A)$$

If Eq. (8.21) is integrated over an interval of time from 0 to t, the relation for $\langle X^2 \rangle_{av}$ is obtained:

$$\langle X^2 \rangle_{av} = 2\langle v_p{}^2 \rangle_{av}\int_0^t dt_2 \int_0^{t_2} R_L\, dt_1. \qquad (8.22)$$

The correlation coefficient R_L gives the statistical relation between the particle velocity measured at two different intervals of time, t and t_1, and the mean square particle velocity. In a case of Brownian motion or of a turbulent field where the particle ve-

[3] In general, the Lagrangian velocity does not equal the Eulerian velocity of the fluid (see also p. 48).
[4] Using the well known *ergodic hypothesis*, certain kinds of averages, taken over the realizations of the behavior of many particles, are assumed equal to the average of the behavior of one particle over a long period of time.

locity varies randomly with time, R_L will only approach unity if the time difference Δt $(= t - t_1)$ approaches zero. As the interval $t - t_1$ becomes larger, the velocity, of the particle will have less connection with its velocity at the beginning of the interval. That is, the value of the correlation coefficient will approach zero as Δt becomes very large. In other words R_L expresses physically the ability of the particle to "remember" its original velocity as it travels farther away from the beginning of its flight path.

In circumstances where small intervals of time are involved, $R_L \approx 1$, and

$$(\Delta t \to 0) \quad \langle X^2 \rangle_{\mathrm{av}} \approx \langle v_p{}^2 \rangle_{\mathrm{av}} (\Delta t)^2. \tag{8.23}$$

As the time interval becomes large, R_L will be finite, and it will depend on Δt, making the integral in (8.22) difficult to evaluate. However, for very large time intervals the integral

$$\int_0^{t_2} R_L \, dt_1 \approx \mathrm{const.} = C,$$

and Eq. (8.22) then will read

$$(\Delta t \to \infty) \quad \langle X^2 \rangle_{\mathrm{av}} \cong 2 \langle v_p{}^2 \rangle_{\mathrm{av}} C \, \Delta t. \tag{8.24}$$

Thus, by comparing Eq. (8.17) with Eq. (8.24), we find that Einstein's diffusivity for Brownian motion represents a limiting case for particle dispersion in a field of turbulent motion. When the time interval is sufficiently large that effectively no correlation exists between the particle velocities at different times, the Einstein diffusivity for turbulent mixing takes the form

$$D = \langle v_p{}^2 \rangle_{\mathrm{av}}{}^{1/2} [\langle v_p{}^2 \rangle_{\mathrm{av}}{}^{1/2} C]. \tag{8.25}$$

For diffusion of molecules by Brownian agitation in a stagnant gas, $\langle v_p{}^2 \rangle_{\mathrm{av}}{}^{1/2} C$ is related to a length parameter proportional to the mean free path of the gas. Then, for turbulent media $\langle v_p{}^2 \rangle_{\mathrm{av}}{}^{1/2} C$ is identified with the mixing length $\mathcal{L}$, and Eq. (8.25) is a direct analogy to Eq. (8.4), the relation for the eddy viscosity. Thus, in analogy to the Einstein diffusivity, the eddy diffusivity for transfer of matter in turbulent media is written as

$$\mathcal{E}_{\mathrm{m}} = \frac{\langle X^2 \rangle_{\mathrm{av}}}{2 \Delta t} = \langle v_p{}^2 \rangle_{\mathrm{av}} \int_0^{t_2} R_L \, dt_1. \tag{8.26}$$

Like the eddy viscosity defined in Eq. (8.3), the eddy diffusivity is not a physical property of the gas, but depends on the nature of the field of turbulence. This is in direct contrast to the molecular diffusivity in gases, which is a physical property depending on the molecules of gas alone.

The character of turbulent dispersion can be illustrated quali- tatively in the photograph of the smoke plume in Plate VII(B). Time in this case is related to a distance x from the stack and the velocity of the wind U by $\Delta t = \Delta x/U$. The plume begins to spread approximately linearly with Δt very near the stack as predicted by Eq (8.23). Farther away, the plume tends to become roughly parabolic in shape and $X \propto (\Delta t)^{1/2}$ given by Eq. (8.24). The para- bolic curvature for large Δt can be seen better by placing a ruler parallel to the outer edges of the plume in Plate VII(B).

Dispersion in non-isotropic turbulence depends on the Lagran- gian velocity field, which can vary with time at each point x in the fluid. The mathematical description of this more realistic case is much more difficult, and the theoretical solution to this problem remains to be found.

In discussing diffusion by continuous movements, we have as- sumed that the particles carried by the fluid were small enough to follow the fluid motion. When larger particles of dust or water droplets are considered, they may not exactly follow the fluid because of their inertia. The study of dispersion of these materials is exceedingly complicated, and still remains largely another unresolved problem in fluid mechanics.

Problems for Thought and Discussion

1. A single wire hot-wire anemometer can measure one component of velocity in a turbulent medium. By geometric schemes, could one construct an anemometer to measure two components of velocity simultaneously? [Hint: See Hinze, *Turbulence*, McGraw-Hill Book Co., Inc., New York, 1959), Chapter 2.]

2. From Eqs. (3.10) and (3.6) derive the approximations for the stability given in Eqs. (3.11) and (3.11A). [Hint: Rearrange Eq. (3.10) in terms of S', use the equilibrium pressure ratio, and rewrite the resulting relation in terms of a binomial expansion. For small vertical displacements of air, terms like $[(g\rho_0/p_0)(z_1 - z_0)]^2$ and higher order can be disregarded.]

3. How high should a weightless, constant-volume balloon, filled with helium at normal atmospheric presure, rise into the atmosphere?

4. Why does the hot-wire anemometer have to be so small in diameter?

5. Deduce Kelvin's theorem, Eq. (4.8), from Bjerknes' relation, Eq. (4.7).

6. Based on the discussions in Chapters 5 and 7, try your luck at forecasting weather in your geographical region for a day or two ahead of time. Compare your prognoses with the experts at the Weather Bureau.

7. Should it be possible to construct a sonic anemometer that

will measure vertical velocity of air and air temperature simultaneously? [Hint: See R. G. Fleagle and J. A. Businger, *Introduction to Atmospheric Physics* (Academic Press, New York, 1963), p. 294.]

8. From Eq. (5.6), deduce the relation between the changes in the Coriolis parameter and the wavelength of inertial waves in a homogeneous atmosphere [Eq. (5.8)]. [Hint: See H. R. Byers, *General Meteorology* (McGraw-Hill Book Co., Inc., New York, 1959), 3rd Ed., pp. 411-412.]

9. What would happen to the thermal circulation induced in a rotating pan, heated at the rim and cooled at the center, if a sloping bottom were introduced into the pan?

10. Using the principles of vorticity discussed in Chapter 4, devise a simple explanation for the observed motion of the great red spot observed in Jupiter's atmosphere. (Hint: See R. Hide, "Origin of Jupiter's Great Red Spot," *Nature* **190,** 895-896.)

11. What may happen to the patterns of atmospheric motion over many centuries if the carbon dioxide content of the atmosphere continues to increase with the geographical spread of technology: (Hint: Carbon dioxide absorbs thermal radiation strongly in wavelengths similar to those of water vapor.)

12. It often has been suggested that one could modify the patterns of weather in the Northern Hemisphere by damming up the Bering Straits. What is the reasoning behind this idea?

13. Los Angeles is plagued by air pollution partly because (a) the atmosphere tends to develop inversions near the earth's surface over the city, reducing vertical motion and trapping the pollutants, and (b) because the mountain ranges to the east of the city block the flow of air to the eastward. To modify the meteorological situation around Los Angeles, it has been suggested that fires over surface layer, unpopulated areas be started during periods of heavy smog, and that giant tunnels containing fans be dug into the mountains. Are these ideas reasonable? Are they practical?

14. Calculate the magnitude of the deflection and its direction for an air particle traveling at 100 mph along latitude 45°N. The earth's rotational speed is 7×10^{-5} radians per second.

15. Planetary waves can develop in both a barotropic atmosphere and a baroclinic atmosphere. How might one distinguish between the orographic origins and thermal origins of a standing wave observed to the eastward of the southern portion of South America?

16. Try deriving Kolmogoroff's relation for the inertial sub-range of the spectrum of turbulent energy from dimensional arguments.

17. Would you expect Kolmogoroff's law for the turbulent energy spectrum to hold in a strongly stably stratified medium? What might eddies look like in stably stratified flow?

18. Try constructing a simple model of a tornado vortex using soda water, a graduated cylinder and a turntable from a record player.

19. The burning of a candle flame depends on circulation of air into and out of the zone of combustion by natural convection. Would a candle burn in an artificial satellite of the earth?

20. The prevailing surface currents observed on the oceans are believed to be wind driven. Considering the structure of the large-scale patterns of winds, discuss this theory. [Hint: See W. S. Von Arx, *Introduction to Physical Oceanography* (Addison-Wesley Publishing Co., Inc., Reading, Massachusetts, 1962).]

For Further Reading

FLUID MECHANICS

1. Prandtl, L., *Essentials of Fluid Dynamics* (Hafner Publishing Co., New York, 1952).
2. Schlichting, H., *Boundary Layer Theory*, trans. by J. Kestin (McGraw-Hill Book Co., Inc., New York, 1960), 4th Ed.
3. Scorer, R. S., *Natural Aerodynamics* (Pergamon Press, Inc., New York, 1958).
4. Shapiro, A. H., *Shape and Flow* (Anchor Books, Doubleday & Co., Inc., Garden City, New York, 1961).

GEOPHYSICS

1. Strahler, A. N., *The Earth Sciences* (Harper and Row Publishers, New York, 1963).

METEOROLOGY

1. Byers, H. R., *General Meteorology* (McGraw-Hill Book Co., Inc., New York, 1959), 3rd Ed.
2. Hess, S. L., *Introduction to Theoretical Meteorology* (Henry Holt and Co., New York, 1959.
3. Riehl, H., *Tropical Meteorology* (McGraw-Hill Book Co., Inc., New York, 1954).

PERIODICALS

Many of the research papers relevant to atmospheric and hydrospheric motion are published in the following journals:

1. Journal of Atmospheric Sciences (American Meteorological Society)
2. Journal of Fluid Mechanics (Cambridge University Press)
3. Journal of Geophysical Research (American Geophysical Union)
4. Tellus (Svenska Geofysiska Foreningen)

Index